5B

Math in Focus®
Singapore Math®
by Marshall Cavendish

Reteach

Author
Dr Fong Ho Kheong

Marshall Cavendish
Education

U.S. Distributor

Houghton Mifflin Harcourt

Published by Marshall Cavendish Education
An imprint of Marshall Cavendish Education Private Limited
Times Centre, 1 New Industrial Road, Singapore 536196
Customer Service Hotline: (65) 6213 9444
U.S. Office Tel: (1-914) 332 8888 Fax: (1-914) 332 8882
E-mail: tmesales@mceducation.com
Website: www.mceducation.com

Distributed by
Houghton Mifflin Harcourt
222 Berkeley Street
Boston, MA 02116
Tel: 617-351-5000
Website: www.hmheducation.com/mathinfocus

First published 2015

Math in Focus® Reteach 5B
ISBN 978-0-544-19256-0

Printed in Singapore

1 2 3 4 5 6 7 8   1401   20 19 18 17 16 15
4500463652   A B C D E

Contents

Graphs and Probability

Angles

Properties of Triangles and Four-Sided Figures

CHAPTER 14

Surface Area and Volume

Introducing

Math in Focus®

Reteach

Reteach 5A and 5B, written to complement *Math in Focus®: Singapore Math® by Marshall Cavendish* Grade 5, offer a second opportunity to practice skills and concepts at the entry level. Key vocabulary terms are explained in context, complemented by sample problems with clearly worked solutions.

Not all children are able to master a new concept or skill after the first practice. A second opportunity to practice at the same level before moving on can be key to long-term success.

Monitor students' levels of understanding during daily instruction and as they work on Practice exercises. Provide *Reteach* worksheets for extra support to students who would benefit from further practice at a basic level.

CHAPTER 8 Decimals

Worksheet 1   Understanding Thousandths

Write the decimal shown by each arrow.

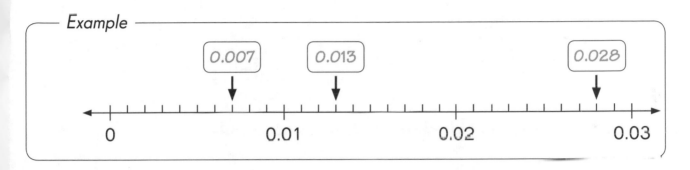

Example

| 0.007 | 0.013 | | 0.028 |

0   0.01   0.02   0.03

1.

0   0.01   0.02   0.03

Find the decimal that the shaded part represents.

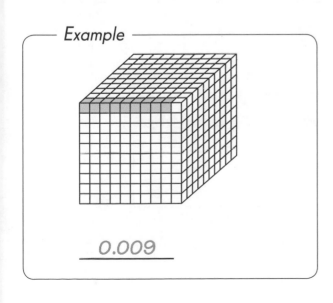

Example

0.009

2.

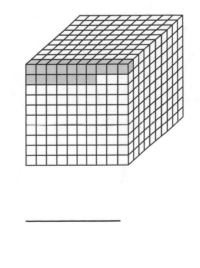

_____

Name: _____ Date: _____

Shade the correct number of cubes to show each decimal.

3. 0.004

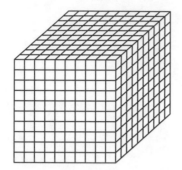

4. 0.028

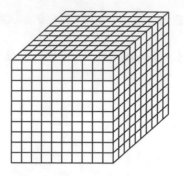

Complete the place-value chart to show the decimal.

Example

0.016

Ones		Tenths	Hundredths	Thousandths
	.		⬤	⬤ ⬤ ⬤ ⬤ ⬤ ⬤

5. 0.258

Ones		Tenths	Hundredths	Thousandths
	.			

Write the decimal shown in the place-value chart.

Example

Ones		Tenths	Hundredths	Thousandths
	•		○ ○ ○	○ ○ ○ ○

_____0.034_____

6.

Ones		Tenths	Hundredths	Thousandths
○	•	○ ○ ○ ○	○ ○	○ ○ ○

_____

Complete.

Example

33 hundredths = 3 tenths _____3_____ hundredths

7.   70 thousandths = _____ hundredths

8.   5 tenths 4 hundredths = _____ thousandths

9.   6 hundredths = _____ thousandths

10.   375 thousandths = _____ hundredths _____ thousandths

Complete.

> *Example*
>
> 4 hundredths 9 thousandths = _0.049_

11. 10 hundredths 7 thousandths = _____

12. 2 hundredths 15 thousandths = _____

13. 38 hundredths 13 thousandths = _____

14. 3 hundredths 8 thousandths = _____

Write each fraction as a decimal.

> *Example*
>
> $\frac{16}{1000}$ = _0.016_
>
> $\frac{16}{1000}$ is equivalent to 0.016.

15. $\frac{7}{1000}$ = _____

16. $\frac{219}{1000}$ = _____

17. $\frac{35}{1000}$ = _____

18. $\frac{146}{1000}$ = _____

Write each mixed number as a decimal.

> **Example**
>
> $3\frac{16}{1000} =$ ___3.016___

19. $2\frac{5}{1000} =$ _____

20. $4\frac{391}{1000} =$ _____

21. $3\frac{56}{1000} =$ _____

22. $1\frac{108}{1000} =$ _____

**4.052 can be written in expanded form as 4 ones and 0 tenths
5 hundredths 2 thousandths.
Write each decimal in expanded notation.**

23. 2.815 = _____ ones and _____ tenths _____ hundredth

_____ thousandths

24. 2.409 = _____ ones and _____ tenths _____ hundredths

_____ thousandths

25. 7.093 = _____ ones and _____ tenths _____ hundredths

_____ thousandths

6.359 can be written in expanded form as 6 + 0.3 + 0.05 + 0.009.
Write each decimal in expanded notation.

26.   4.273 = _____ + _____ + _____ + _____

27.   1.503 = _____ + _____ + _____

28.   9.017 = _____ + _____ + _____

2.478 can be written in expanded form as $2 + \dfrac{4}{10} + \dfrac{7}{100} + \dfrac{8}{1000}$.
Write each decimal in expanded notation.

29. $3.165 = 3 + \dfrac{\boxed{}}{10} + \dfrac{\boxed{}}{100} + \dfrac{\boxed{}}{1000}$

30. $5.294 = \underline{\hspace{2cm}} + \dfrac{2}{\boxed{}} + \dfrac{9}{\boxed{}} + \dfrac{4}{\boxed{}}$

31. $4.758 = \underline{\hspace{2cm}} + \dfrac{\boxed{}}{10} + \dfrac{5}{\boxed{}} + \dfrac{\boxed{}}{1000}$

32. $6.094 = \underline{\hspace{2cm}} + \dfrac{\boxed{}}{100} + \dfrac{4}{\boxed{}}$

33. $7.506 = \underline{\hspace{2cm}} + \dfrac{\boxed{}}{10} + \dfrac{\boxed{}}{\boxed{}}$

Fill in the blanks.

In 4.702:

34. The digit 7 is in the _____ place.

35. The digit 4 is in the _____ place.

36. The digit 2 is in the _____ place.

37. The digit 0 is in the _____ place.

In 6.908:

38. The value of the digit 9 is _____.

39. The value of the digit 0 is _____.

40. The value of the digit 8 is _____.

41. The value of the digit 6 is _____.

In 7.035:

42. The digit 3 stands for _____.

43. The digit 0 is in the _____ place.

44. The digit 5 is in the _____ place.

45. The value of the digit 7 is _____.

Solve.

46.   The digit 9 stands for 9 ones.
The digit 7 is in the tenths place.
The value of the digit 4 is 0.04.
The digit 2 is in the thousandths place.
What is the decimal?

47.   The value of the digit 8 is 0.8.
The digit 1 stands for 1 hundredth.
The digit 5 is in the ones place.
The value of the digit 4 is 0.004.
Find the decimal.

Worksheet 2   Comparing and Rounding Decimals

Use the place-value chart to compare the decimals.
Which decimal is greater?

Example

	Ones	Tenths	Hundredths	Thousandths
0.054	0	0	5	4
0.54	0	5	4	0

Compare the ones. Are they the same?   Yes / No   __Yes__

Compare the tenths. Are they the same?   Yes / No   __No__

___5___ tenths > ___0___ tenths

___0.54___ is greater than ___0.054___.

1.

	Ones	Tenths	Hundredths	Thousandths
0.108				
0.12				

Compare the ones. Are they the same?   Yes / No   _____

Compare the tenths. Are they the same?   Yes / No   _____

Compare the hundredths. Are they the same?   Yes / No   _____

_____ hundredths > _____ hundredths

_____ is greater than _____.

Write the greater decimal.

2.   3.4 or 3.9 _____

3.   16.23 or 16.71 _____

4.   105.67 or 105.01 _____

5.   3.03 or 3.19 _____

6.   99.89 or 98.98 _____

7.   0.859 or 0.891 _____

8.   133.2 or 132.0 _____

Use the place-value chart to compare the decimals.
Which decimal is the least?

Example

	Ones	Tenths	Hundredths	Thousandths
2.375	2	3	7	5
2.357	2	3	5	7
2.385	2	3	8	5

Compare the ones. Are they the same?   Yes / No   _Yes_

Compare the tenths. Are they the same?   Yes / No   _Yes_

Compare the hundredths. Are they the same?   Yes / No   _No_

___8___ hundredths > ___7___ hundredths > ___5___ hundredths

The least decimal is _2.357_.

9.

	Ones	Tenths	Hundredths	Thousandths
4.857				
4.852				
4.854				

Compare the ones. Are they the same?   Yes / No   _____

Compare the tenths. Are they the same?   Yes / No   _____

Compare the hundredths. Are they the same?   Yes / No   _____

Compare the thousandths. Are they the same?   Yes / No   _____

_____ thousandths > _____ thousandths > _____ thousandths

The least decimal is _____.

Use the place-value chart to compare the decimals. Which decimal is the greatest?

Example

	Ones	Tenths	Hundredths
3.17	3	1	7
3.08	3	0	8
3.42	3	4	2

Compare the ones. Are they the same?   Yes / No   _Yes_

Compare the tenths. Are they the same?   Yes / No   _No_

_4_ tenths > _1_ tenth > _0_ tenths

The greatest decimal is _3.42_.

10.

	Ones	Tenths	Hundredths	Thousandths
5.273				
5.291				
5.248				

Compare the ones. Are they the same?   Yes / No _____

Compare the tenths. Are they the same?   Yes / No _____

Compare the hundredths. Are they the same?   Yes / No _____

_____ hundredths > _____ hundredths > _____ hundredths

The greatest decimal is _____.

Cross out the greatest decimal and circle the least.

11.   1.49   1.418   1.814

12.   0.37   0.312   0.366

13.   8.01   8.108   8.181

14.   21.71   27.1   21.07

15.   2.59   2.81   2.95

16.   7.12   7.22   7.17

17.   0.604   0.641   0.601

Use the place-value chart to order the decimals from least to greatest.

Example

	Ones	Tenths	Hundredths	Thousandths
0.09	0	0	9	0
0.209	0	2	0	9
2.009	2	0	0	9

Compare the ones. Are they the same?   Yes / No   __No__

Compare the tenths. Are they the same?   Yes / No   __No__

___0.09___ , ___0.209___ , ___2.009___
  least   greatest

18.

	Ones	Tenths	Hundredths	Thousandths
3.586				
0.314				
3.567				

Compare the ones. Are they the same?   Yes / No   _____

Compare the tenths. Are they the same?   Yes / No   _____

Compare the hundredths. Are they the same?   Yes / No   _____

_____ , _____ , _____
  least   greatest

Order the decimals from least to greatest.

19. 0.103,   0.311,   0.131   _____

20. 5.14,   0.15,   1.44   _____

21. 7.013,   7.131,   7.033   _____

22. 9.090,   9.900,   9.009   _____

23. 0.081,   0.118,   0.180   _____

24. 3.963,   3.936,   3.639   _____

25. 9.449,   4.949,   9.494   _____

26. 6.02,   2.06,   0.62   _____

Use the place-value chart to order the decimals from greatest to least.

Example

	Ones	**Tenths**	**Hundredths**	**Thousandths**
0.426	0	4	2	6
0.5	0	5	0	0
0.19	0	1	9	0

Compare the ones. Are they the same?   Yes / No   ___Yes___

Compare the tenths. Are they the same?   Yes / No   ___No___

___0.5___, ___0.426___, ___0.19___
greatest   least

27.

	Ones	Tenths	Hundredths	Thousandths
2.396				
1.431				
2.302				

Compare the ones. Are they the same?   Yes / No   _____

Compare the tenths. Are they the same?   Yes / No   _____

Compare the hundredths. Are they the same?   Yes / No   _____

_____, _____, _____

greatest   least

Order the decimals from greatest to least.

28.   21.12,   12.21,   12.12   _____

29.   0.101,   0.011,   0.110   _____

30.   4.63,   4.36,   4.06   _____

Show the location of each decimal by drawing an X on the number line. Then round the decimal to the nearest hundredth.

31.

0.14   0.15

0.148 rounded to the nearest hundredth is _____.

32.

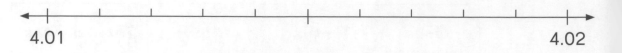

4.01   4.02

4.013 rounded to the nearest hundredth is _____.

Round each decimal to the nearest whole number, nearest tenth, and nearest hundredth.

	Decimal	Rounded to the Nearest		
		Whole Number	Tenth	Hundredth
33.	0.147			
34.	2.564			
35.	6.325			

Fill in the blanks.

36.   I am thinking of a decimal. It is 2.77 when rounded to the nearest hundredth. It is smaller than 2.77. What could this decimal be?

_____

37.   1 square meter is equal to 1.195 square yards.
Round 1.195 square yards to the nearest hundredth.

_____

Worksheet 3   Rewriting Decimals as Fractions and Mixed Numbers

Rewrite each decimal as a fraction or mixed number in simplest form.

Example

$$0.007 = \frac{7}{1000}$$

---

1. $0.8 =$ _____

2. $5.9 =$ _____

3. $6.04 =$ _____

4. $0.47 =$ _____

5. $0.072 =$ _____

6. $7.015 =$ _____

7. $2.436 =$ _____

8. $2.037 =$ _____

9. $4.008 =$ _____

10. $16.15 =$ _____

11. $0.754 =$ _____

12. 0.005 = _____

13. 4.36 = _____

14. 0.02 = _____

15. 12.06 = _____

16. 11.008 = _____

17. 15.052 = _____

18. 17.814 = _____

19. 19.3 = _____

20. 9.405 = _____

21. 0.108 = _____

22. 4.7 = _____

23. 0.3 = _____

24. 1.345 = _____

25. 0.539 = _____

CHAPTER 9 Multiplying and Dividing Decimals

Worksheet 1   Multiplying Decimals

Multiply. Write the product as a decimal.

Example

2 tenths × 3 = _____6_____ tenths

So, 0.2 × 3 = _____6_____ tenths

= _____0.6_____ .

The **product** is 0.6.

---

1.   4 tenths × 2 = _____ tenths

So, 0.4 × 2 = _____ tenths

= _____ .

2.   3 tenths × 3 = _____ tenths

So, 0.3 × 3 = _____ tenths

= _____ .

3.   8 tenths × 5 = _____ tenths

So, 0.8 × 5 = _____ tenths

= _____ .

4.   4 tenths × 4 = _____ tenths

So, 0.4 × 4 = _____ tenths

= _____ .

5.   6 tenths × 7 = _____ tenths

So, 0.6 × 7 = _____ tenths

= _____ .

Multiply.

> **Example**
>
> 0.2 × 4 = ___0.8___

6.   0.3 × 2 = _____   **7.**   0.3 × 4 = _____

8.   0.4 × 6 = _____

Multiply.

> **Example**
>
> $$\begin{array}{r} 0.3 \\ \times\quad 3 \\ \hline 0.9 \end{array}$$

9. $\begin{array}{r} 0.6 \\ \times\quad 4 \\ \hline \end{array}$ **10.** $\begin{array}{r} 0.5 \\ \times\quad 8 \\ \hline \end{array}$ **11.** $\begin{array}{r} 0.7 \\ \times\quad 3 \\ \hline \end{array}$ **12.** $\begin{array}{r} 0.9 \\ \times\quad 5 \\ \hline \end{array}$

Fill in the blanks.

> *Example*
>
> 2 ones + 50 tenths = ___7 ones___

13.   4 ones + 20 tenths = _____ ones

14.   6 ones + 30 tenths = _____ ones

15.   9 ones + 40 tenths = _____ ones

Fill in the blanks.

> *Example*
>
> 12 tenths = ___1___ ones and ___2___ tenths

16.   24 tenths = _____ ones and _____ tenths

17.   37 tenths = _____ ones and _____ tenths

18.   101 tenths = _____ ones and _____ tenth

Multiply. Fill in the blanks.

> *Example*
>
> 4 tenths $\times$ 3 = ____12____ tenths
>
> = ____1____ one and ____2____ tenths

19. 6 tenths $\times$ 4 = _____ tenths

= _____ ones and _____ tenths

20. 5 tenths $\times$ 7 = _____ tenths

= _____ ones and _____ tenths

21. 8 tenths $\times$ 6 = _____ tenths

= _____ ones and _____ tenths

Multiply. Fill in the blanks.

> *Example*
>
> 2 ones and 4 tenths $\times$ 2 = ____4____ ones and ____8____ tenths

22. 3 ones and 2 tenths $\times$ 4 = _____ ones and _____ tenths

23. 7 ones and 1 tenth $\times$ 6 = _____ ones and _____ tenths

24. 6 ones and 3 tenths $\times$ 3 = _____ ones and _____ tenths

Multiply. Fill in the blanks.

┌─ Example ───┐

2.8 × 5   →   8 tenths × 5 = ___40___ tenths

___40___ tenths = ___4___ ones and ___0___ tenths

2 ones × 5 = ___10___ ones

___4___ ones + ___10___ ones = ___14___ ones

So, 2.8 × 5 = ___14.0___.

└───┘

Multiply 4.7 by 3. Fill in the blanks.

25.   4.7 × 3   →   7 tenths × 3 = _____ tenths

_____ tenths = _____ ones and _____ tenth

4 ones × 3 = _____ ones

_____ ones + _____ ones = _____ ones

So, 4.7 × 3 = _____.

Multiply 5.6 by 4. Fill in the blanks.

26.   5.6 × 4   →   6 tenths × 4 = _____ tenths

_____ tenths = _____ ones and _____ tenths

5 ones × 4 = _____ ones

_____ ones + _____ ones = _____ ones

So, 5.6 × 4 = _____.

Multiply 6.8 by 7. Fill in the blanks.

27.   6.8 × 7 → 8 tenths × 7 = _____ tenths

_____ tenths = _____ ones and _____ tenths

6 ones × 7 = _____ ones

_____ ones + _____ ones = _____ ones

So, 6.8 × 7 = _____.

Multiply 3.7 by 4. Fill in the blanks.

28.   3.7 × 4 → 7 tenths × 4 = _____ tenths

_____ tenths = _____ ones and _____ tenths

3 ones × 4 = _____ ones

_____ ones + _____ ones = _____ ones

So, 3.7 × 4 = _____.

Multiply 1.6 by 6. Fill in the blanks.

29.   1.6 × 6 → 6 tenths × 6 = _____ tenths

_____ tenths = _____ ones and _____ tenths

1 one × 6 = _____ ones

_____ ones + _____ ones = _____ ones

So, 1.6 × 6 = _____.

Multiply.

30.   2.8
       $\times$ 8
       _____

31.   4.7
       $\times$ 7
       _____

32.   6.9
       $\times$ 2
       _____

Multiply. Write the product as a decimal.

> **Example**
>
> 3 hundredths $\times$ 2 = ____6____ hundredths
>
> So, 0.03 $\times$ 2 = ____6____ hundredths
>
> = ___0.06___ .

33. 3 hundredths $\times$ 3 = _____ hundredths

So, 0.03 $\times$ 3 = _____ hundredths

= _____ .

34. 2 hundredths $\times$ 4 = _____ hundredths

So, 0.02 $\times$ 4 = _____ hundredths

= _____ .

Multiply. Write the product as a decimal.

35. $0.02 \times 3 = $ _____

36. $0.03 \times 4 = $ _____

37. $0.04 \times 4 = $ _____

38. $0.01 \times 5 = $ _____

Fill in the blanks.

> *Example*
>
> 23 hundredths = _____ 2 _____ tenths _____ 3 _____ hundredths

39. 47 hundredths = _____ tenths _____ hundredths

40. 80 hundredths = _____ tenths _____ hundredths

41. 59 hundredths = _____ tenths _____ hundredths

Fill in the blanks.

42. 4 hundredths + 8 hundredths = _____ hundredths

= _____ tenth _____ hundredths

43. 9 hundredths + 5 hundredths = _____ hundredths

= _____ tenth _____ hundredths

Multiply. Fill in the blanks.

> **Example**
>
> 5 hundredths × 3 = ___15___ hundredths
>
> = ___1___ tenth ___5___ hundredths

44. 4 hundredths × 7 = _____ hundredths

= _____ tenths _____ hundredths

45. 6 hundredths × 8 = _____ hundredths

= _____ tenths _____ hundredths

Multiply.

46. $\begin{array}{r} 0.04 \\ \times\quad 3 \\ \hline \end{array}$ **47.** $\begin{array}{r} 0.02 \\ \times\quad 9 \\ \hline \end{array}$

48. $\begin{array}{r} 0.05 \\ \times\quad 3 \\ \hline \end{array}$ **49.** $\begin{array}{r} 0.04 \\ \times\quad 5 \\ \hline \end{array}$

Multiply. Fill in the blanks.

> **Example**
>
> 4 tenths 2 hundredths × 2 = ___8___ tenths +
>
> ___0___ tenths ___4___ hundredths
>
> = ___8___ tenths ___4___ hundredths

50.   1 tenth 4 hundredths × 6 = _____ tenths +

                           _____ tenths _____ hundredths

                     = _____ tenths _____ hundredths

51.   2 tenths 3 hundredths × 7 = _____ tenths +

                           _____ tenths _____ hundredth

                     = _____ tenths _____ hundredth

52.   3 tenths 2 hundredths × 8 = _____ tenths +

                           _____ tenth _____ hundredths

                     = _____ tenths _____ hundredths

Multiply. Fill in the blanks.

> **Example**
>
> 8 hundredths × 3 = ____24____ hundredths
>
>   = ____2____ tenths ____4____ hundredths
>
> So, 0.08 × 3 = ____0.24____.

Multiply 0.05 by 7. Fill in the blanks.

53.   5 hundredths × 7 = _____ hundredths

                     = _____ tenths _____ hundredths

    So, 0.05 × 7 = _____.

Multiply 0.49 by 2. Fill in the blanks.

54. 9 hundredths $\times$ 2 = _____ hundredths

_____ hundredths = _____ tenth _____ hundredths

4 tenths $\times$ 2 = _____ tenths

_____ tenth + _____ tenths = _____ tenths

_____ tenths = _____ ones and _____ tenths

So, 0.49 $\times$ 2 = _____.

Multiply 0.25 by 3. Fill in the blanks.

55. 5 hundredths $\times$ 3 = _____ hundredths

_____ hundredths = _____ tenth _____ hundredths

2 tenths $\times$ 3 = _____ tenths

_____ tenth + _____ tenths = _____ tenths

_____ tenths = _____ ones and _____ tenths

So, 0.25 $\times$ 3 = _____.

Multiply 0.43 by 4. Fill in the blanks.

56. 3 hundredths $\times$ 4 = _____ hundredths

_____ hundredths = _____ tenth _____ hundredths

4 tenths $\times$ 4 = _____ tenths

_____ tenth + _____ tenths = _____ tenths

_____ tenths = _____ one and _____ tenths

So, 0.43 $\times$ 4 = _____.

Multiply 0.67 by 5. Fill in the blanks.

57.   7 hundredths $\times$ 5 = _____ hundredths

      _____ hundredths = _____ tenths _____ hundredths

      6 tenths $\times$ 5 = _____ tenths

      _____ tenths + _____ tenths = _____ tenths

      _____ tenths = _____ ones and _____ tenths

      So, 0.67 $\times$ 5 = _____.

Multiply.

58.   1.45

         $\times$ 3

         ———

59.   2.36

         $\times$ 4

         ———

60.   3.58

         $\times$ 6

         ———

Worksheet 2   Multiplying by Tens, Hundreds, or Thousands

Place the decimal point in the correct place in the product.

> **Example**
>
> $4.35 \times 10 = 4\ 3\ .\ 5$
>
> When you multiply a decimal by 10, move the decimal point 1 decimal place to the right.

1. $1.28 \times 10 - 1\ 2\ 8$

2. $4.75 \times 10 = 4\ 7\ 5$

3. $0.36 \times 10 = 3\ 6$

4. $0.92 \times 10 = 9\ 2$

5. $3.45 \times 10 = 3\ 4\ 5$

6. $0.81 \times 10 = 8\ 1$

7. $6.4 \times 10 = 6\ 4$

8. $7.8 \times 10 = 7\ 8$

9. $0.7 \times 10 = 7$

10. $0.9 \times 10 = 9$

11. $5.3 \times 10 = 5\ 3$

12. $0.4 \times 10 = 4$

13. $0.375 \times 10 = 3\ 7\ 5$

14. $0.284 \times 10 = 2\ 8\ 4$

15. $1.693 \times 10 = 1\ 6\ 9\ 3$

16. $2.438 \times 10 = 2\ 4\ 3\ 8$

17. $0.736 \times 10 = 7\ 3\ 6$

18. $8.931 \times 10 = 8\ 9\ 3\ 1$

Multiply.

19. $1.39 \times 10 =$ _____

20. $2.47 \times 10 =$ _____

21. $0.84 \times 10 =$ _____

22. $0.94 \times 10 =$ _____

23. $7.2 \times 10 =$ _____

24. $6.3 \times 10 =$ _____

25. $0.8 \times 10 =$ _____

26. $0.2 \times 10 =$ _____

27. $0.481 \times 10 =$ _____

28. $0.179 \times 10 =$ _____

29. $2.435 \times 10 =$ _____

30. $6.582 \times 10 =$ _____

Complete.

31. $0.478 \times$ _____ $= 4.78$

32. $0.07 \times$ _____ $= 0.7$

33. $0.59 \times$ _____ $= 5.9$

34. $0.26 \times$ _____ $= 2.6$

35. _____ $\times 10 = 12.08$

36. _____ $\times 10 = 1.03$

37. _____ $\times 10 = 3.05$

38. _____ $\times 10 = 245.8$

39. $40 =$ _____ $\times 10$

40. $70 = 7 \times$ _____

41. $150 =$ _____ $\times 10$

42. $120 = 12 \times$ _____

43. $8 \times$ _____ $= 80$

44. _____ $\times 10 = 90$

45. $16 \times$ _____ $= 160$

46. _____ $\times 10 = 170$

Complete.

> *Example*
>
> $5 \times 40 = 5 \times \underline{\quad 4 \quad} \times 10$
>
> $= \underline{\quad 20 \quad} \times 10$
>
> $= \underline{\quad 200 \quad}$

47. $6 \times 70 = 6 \times \underline{\qquad} \times 10$

$= \underline{\qquad} \times 10$

$= \underline{\qquad}$

48. $8 \times 120 = \underline{\qquad} \times \underline{\qquad} \times 10$

$= \underline{\qquad} \times 10$

$= \underline{\qquad}$

49. $11 \times 50 = \underline{\qquad} \times \underline{\qquad} \times 10$

$= \underline{\qquad} \times 10$

$= \underline{\qquad}$

50. $16 \times 180 = \underline{\qquad} \times \underline{\qquad} \times 10$

$= \underline{\qquad} \times 10$

$= \underline{\qquad}$

Find each product.

> *Example*
>
> 0.6 × 80 = ____48____
>
> 0.6 × 8 = 4.8
> 0.6 × 80 = 48

51.   0.7 × 90 = _____

52.   0.9 × 50 = _____

53.   0.12 × 40 = _____

54.   0.13 × 60 = _____

55.   0.15 × 50 = _____

56.   0.18 × 30 = _____

57.   7.258 × 100 = _____

58.   3.295 × 200 = _____

59.   0.471 × 300 = _____

60.   0.0384 × 400 = _____

Place the decimal point in the correct place in the product.

> **Example**
>
> 2.54 × 100 = 2 5 4.
>
> When you multiply a decimal by 100, move the decimal point 2 decimal places to the right.

61.   1.375 × 100 = 1 3 7 5

62.   2.679 × 100 = 2 6 7 9

63.   0.472 × 100 = 4 7 2

64.   0.814 × 100 = 8 1 4

65.   5.78 × 100 = 5 7 8

66.   6.93 × 100 = 6 9 3

67.   0.38 × 100 = 3 8

68.   0.91 × 100 = 9 1

69.   6.3792 × 1,000 =

70.   4.1835 × 1,000 =

71.   0.0384 × 1,000 =

72.   0.0172 × 1,000 =

Place the decimal point in the correct place in the product.

> *Example*
>
> $$0.213 \times 1{,}000 = 2\ 1\ 3.$$
>
> When you multiply a decimal by 1,000, move the decimal point 3 decimal places to the right.

73. $1.492 \times 1{,}000 = 1\ 4\ 9\ 2$

74. $2.679 \times 1{,}000 = 2\ 6\ 7\ 9$

75. $0.385 \times 1{,}000 = 3\ 8\ 5$

76. $0.496 \times 1{,}000 = 4\ 9\ 6$

77. $4.67 \times 1{,}000 = 4\ 6\ 7$

78. $5.82 \times 1{,}000 = 5\ 8\ 2$

79. $0.4 \times 1{,}000 = 4$

80. $0.1 \times 1{,}000 = 1$

Complete.

81. $0.583 \times \underline{\hspace{2cm}} = 58.3$ **82.** $0.07 \times \underline{\hspace{2cm}} = 70$

83. $0.481 \times \underline{\hspace{2cm}} = 48.1$ **84.** $0.032 \times \underline{\hspace{2cm}} = 32$

85. $\underline{\hspace{2cm}} \times 100 = 36.9$ **86.** $\underline{\hspace{2cm}} \times 1{,}000 = 204$

87. _____ × 1,000 = 48   **88.** _____ × 100 = 91

89. 500 = _____ × 100   **90.** 8,000 = 8 × _____

91. 9,000 = _____ × 1,000   **92.** 1,400 = 14 × _____

93. 7 × _____ = 700   **94.** _____ × 1,000 = 6,000

95. 13 × _____ = 13,000   **96.** _____ × 100 = 2,600

Complete.

> *Example*
>
> $\quad$ 4 × 500 = 4 × ____5____ × 100
>
> $\qquad\qquad$ = ___20___ × 100
>
> $\qquad\qquad$ = __2,000__

97. 3 × 8,000 = 3 × _____ × 1,000

$\qquad\qquad$ = _____ × 1,000

$\qquad\qquad$ = _____

98. 7 × 1,100 = _____ × _____ × 100

$\qquad\qquad$ = _____ × 100

$\qquad\qquad$ = _____

99. 12 × 6,000 = _____ × _____ × 1,000

$\qquad\qquad$ = _____ × 1,000

$\qquad\qquad$ = _____

Name: _____   **Date:** _____

Find each product.

> **Example**
>
> $7 \times 400 =$ ___2,800___
>
> $7 \times 4 = 28$
> $7 \times 400 = 2,800$
>
>

100. $4 \times 8,000 =$ _____

101. $6 \times 900 =$ _____

102. $5 \times 6,000 =$ _____

103. $8 \times 700 =$ _____

Find each product.

> **Example**
>
> $0.37 \times 200 =$ ___74___
>
> $0.37 \times 2 = 0.74$
> $0.37 \times 200 = 74$
>
>

104. $0.13 \times 700 =$ _____

105. $1.2 \times 8,000 =$ _____

106. $1.5 \times 600 =$ _____

107. $0.17 \times 4,000 =$ _____

Name: _____ **Date:** _____

Complete.

108. $10^2 =$ _____ $\times$ _____

109. $10^3 =$ _____ $\times$ _____ $\times$ _____

Simplify.

110. $10 \times 10 \times 10 =$ _____

111. $10 \times 10 =$ _____

Find each product.

Example

2.54 $\times$ 100 = 2 5 4.

When you multiply a decimal by 100, move the decimal point 2 decimal places to the right.

112. $7.258 \times 100 =$ _____

113. $3.295 \times 100 =$ _____

114. $0.471 \times 100 =$ _____

115. $0.0384 \times 100 =$ _____

Find each product.

> *Example*
>
> 0.213 × 1,000 = 2 1 3.
>
> When you multiply a decimal by 1,000, move the decimal point 3 decimal places to the right.

116. 3.792 × 1,000 = _____

117. 1.835 × 1,000 = _____

118. 0.0384 × 1,000 = _____

119. 0.0172 × 1,000 = _____

Find each product.

120. $2.478 \times 10^2 =$ _____

121. $0.587 \times 10^2 =$ _____

122. $1.3695 \times 10^3 =$ _____

123. $0.0478 \times 10^3 =$ _____

Worksheet 3   Dividing Decimals

Divide. Fill in the blanks.

> *Example*
>
> 8 tenths ÷ 2 = _____4_____ tenths
>
> 6 hundredths ÷ 2 = _____3_____ hundredths

1.   9 tenths ÷ 3 = _____ tenths

2.   12 hundredths ÷ 4 = _____ hundredths

3.   25 hundredths ÷ 5 = _____ hundredths

4.   16 tenths ÷ 4 = _____ tenths

5.   28 hundredths ÷ 7 = _____ hundredths

6.   48 hundredths ÷ 6 = _____ hundredths

7.   64 hundredths ÷ 8 = _____ hundredths

8.   92 hundredths ÷ 4 = _____ hundredths

9.   15 tenths ÷ 3 = _____ tenths

10.   24 tenths ÷ 6 = _____ tenths

11.   56 hundredths ÷ 8 = _____ hundredths

12.   70 hundredths ÷ 5 = _____ hundredths

13.   81 hundredths ÷ 9 = _____ hundredths

Name: _____ Date: _____

Divide 0.42 by 6. Fill in the blanks.

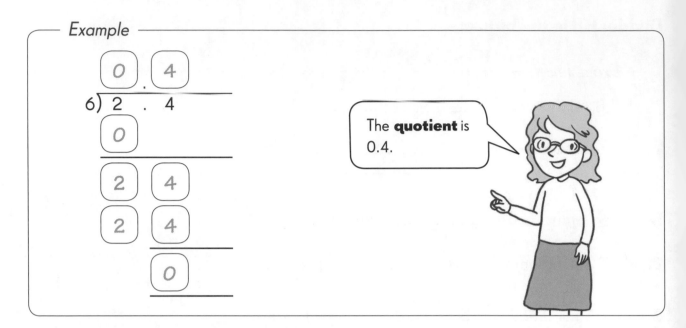

Example

6 ⟌ 2 . 4

| 0 | . | 4 |

0

2 4

2 4

0

The **quotient** is 0.4.

Divide 4.6 by 2. Fill in the blanks.

14.

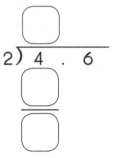

2 ⟌ 4 . 6

Divide the ones by 2.

4 ones ÷ 2 = _____ ones

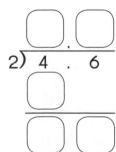

2 ⟌ 4 . 6

Divide the tenths by 2.

6 tenths ÷ 2 = _____ tenths

So, 4.6 ÷ 2 = _____.

42   **Chapter 9** Lesson 9.3

Divide 6.9 by 3. Fill in the blanks.

15.

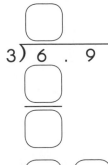

Divide the ones by 3.

6 ones ÷ 3 = _____ ones

Divide the tenths by 3.

9 tenths ÷ 3 = _____ tenths

So, 6.9 ÷ 3 = _____.

Divide 8.4 by 4. Fill in the blanks.

16.

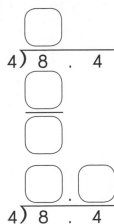

Divide the ones by 4.

8 ones ÷ 4 = _____ ones

Divide the tenths by 4.

4 tenths ÷ 4 = _____ tenth

So, 8.4 ÷ 4 = _____.

Divide.

Example

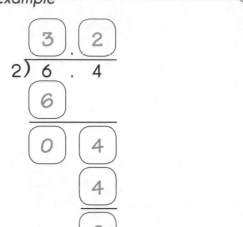

$$
\begin{array}{r}
32 \\
2)\overline{6.4} \\
6 \\
\hline
0.4 \\
4 \\
\hline
0
\end{array}
$$

17.

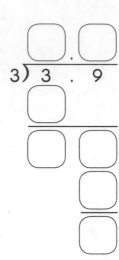

3)3.9

18.

3)2.4

19.

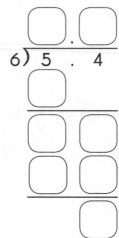

6)5.4

20.

7)0.7

21.

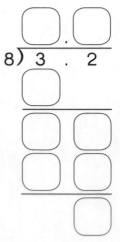

8)3.2

Regroup. Then divide.

> *Example*
>
> 4.29 ÷ 3
>
> 4 ones = _____3_____ ones and 10 tenths
>
> 4 ones and 2 tenths = 3 ones and 10 tenths + 2 tenths
>
> = 3 ones and _____12_____ tenths
>
> 3 ones and _____12_____ tenths 9 hundredths ÷ 3
>
> = _____1_____ one and _____4_____ tenths _____3_____ hundredths

22.   3.68 ÷ 2

3 ones = _____ ones and 10 tenths

3 ones and 6 tenths = _____ ones and 10 tenths + _____ tenths

= _____ ones and _____ tenths

2 ones and _____ tenths _____ hundredths ÷ 2

= _____ one and _____ tenths _____ hundredths

23.   6.54 ÷ 3

5 tenths = _____ tenths 20 hundredths

5 tenths 4 hundredths

= _____ tenths 20 hundredths + _____ hundredths

= _____ tenths _____ hundredths

6 ones and _____ tenths _____ hundredths ÷ 3

= _____ ones and _____ tenth _____ hundredths

24. 4.64 ÷ 4

6 tenths = _____ tenths _____ hundredths

6 tenths 4 hundredths

= _____ tenths _____ hundredths + _____ hundredths

= _____ tenths _____ hundredths

4 ones and _____ tenths _____ hundredths ÷ 4

= _____ one and _____ tenth _____ hundredths

25. 4.95 ÷ 3

4 ones = _____ ones and _____ tenths

9 tenths 5 hundredths

= _____ tenths _____ hundredths + _____ hundredths

= _____ tenths _____ hundredths

3 ones and _____ tenths _____ hundredths ÷ 3

= _____ one and _____ tenths _____ hundredths

26. 6.55 ÷ 5

6 ones = _____ ones and _____ tenths

6 ones and 5 tenths = _____ ones and _____ tenths + _____ tenths

= _____ ones and _____ tenths

5 ones and _____ tenths _____ hundredths ÷ 5

= _____ one and _____ tenths _____ hundredth

Divide 4.56 by 2. Fill in the blanks.

Example

$$\begin{array}{r} 2\\ 2{\overline{)}\,4\ .\ 5\ \ 6}\\ 4\\ \hline 0 \end{array}$$

Divide the ones by 2.

4 ones ÷ 2 = ___2___ ones

$$\begin{array}{r} 2\ .\ 2\\ 2{\overline{)}\,4\ .\ 5\ \ 6}\\ 4\\ \hline 0\ \ 5\\ 4\\ \hline 1 \end{array}$$

Divide the tenths by 2.

5 tenths ÷ 2 = ___2___ tenths R ___1___ tenth

___1___ tenth = ___10___ hundredths

$$\begin{array}{r} 2\ .\ 2\\ 2{\overline{)}\,4\ .\ 5\ \ 6}\\ 4\\ \hline 0\ \ 5\\ 4\\ \hline 1\ \ 6 \end{array}$$

Add the hundredths.

___10___ hundredths + ___6___ hundredths

= ___16___ hundredths

$2) \overline{4 . 5 \ 6}$

$\boxed{2} . \boxed{2} \boxed{8}$

$\boxed{4}$

$\boxed{0} \ \boxed{5}$

$\boxed{4}$

$\boxed{1} \boxed{6}$

$\boxed{1} \boxed{6}$

$\boxed{0}$

Divide the hundredths by 2.

___16___ hundredths ÷ 2

= ___8___ hundredths

So, 4.56 ÷ 2 = ___2.28___.

Divide 6.57 by 3. Fill in the blanks.

27.

$3) \overline{6 . 5 \ 7}$

Divide the ones by 3.

6 ones ÷ 3 = _____ ones

$3) \overline{6 . 5 \ 7}$

Divide the tenths by 3.

5 tenths ÷ 3 = _____ tenth R _____ tenths

_____ tenths = _____ hundredths

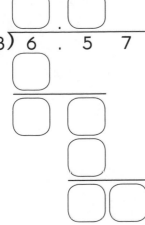

Add the hundredths.

_____ hundredths + _____ hundredths

= _____ hundredths

Divide the hundredths by 3.

_____ hundredths ÷ 3

= _____ hundredths

So, 6.57 ÷ 3 = _____.

Divide.

28.

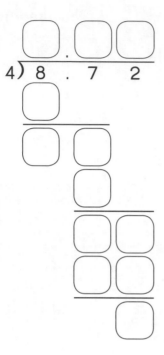

29.

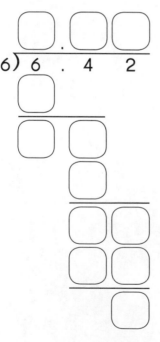

Divide 5.48 by 2. Fill in the blanks.

30.

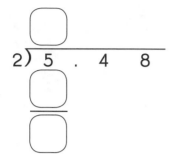

Divide the ones by 2.

5 ones ÷ 2 = _____ ones R _____ one

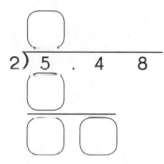

Regroup the remainder _____ one.

_____ one = _____ tenths

Add the tenths.

_____ tenths + _____ tenths = _____ tenths

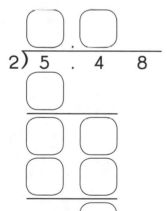

Divide the tenths by 2.

_____ tenths ÷ 2 = _____ tenths

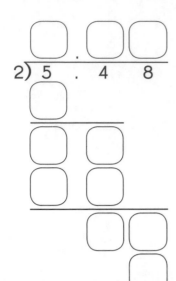

Divide the hundredths by 2.

_____ hundredths ÷ 2

= _____ hundredths

So, 5.48 ÷ 2 = _____.

Divide 6.78 by 3. Fill in the blanks.

31.

3) 6 . 7 8

Divide the ones by 3.

6 ones ÷ 3 = _____ ones

3) 6 . 7 8

Divide the tenths by 3.

_____ tenths ÷ 3 = _____ tenths R _____ tenth

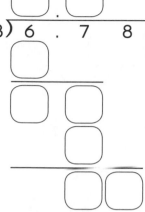

Regroup the remainder ____ tenth.

____ tenth = ____ hundredths

Add the hundredths.

____ hundredths + ____ hundredths

= ____ hundredths

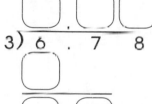

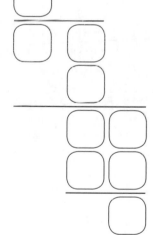

Divide the hundredths by 3.

____ hundredths ÷ 3

= ____ hundredths

So, 6.78 ÷ 3 = _____.

Divide.

32.

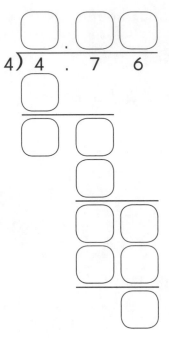

33.

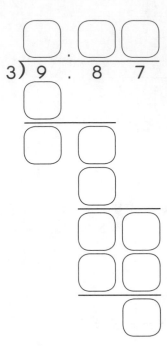

34.

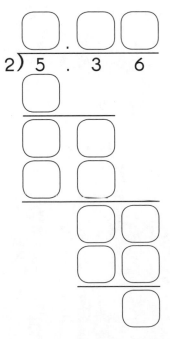

35.

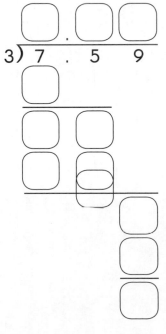

36.

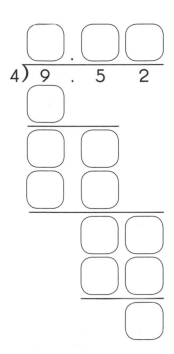

37.

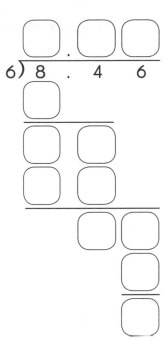

Divide.

38. 0.48 ÷ 2 = _____

39. 0.36 ÷ 2 = _____

40. 4.56 ÷ 2 = _____

41. 1.58 ÷ 2 = _____

42. 3.76 ÷ 2 = _____

43. 0.96 ÷ 3 = _____

44. 0.54 ÷ 3 = _____

45. 6.93 ÷ 3 = _____

46. 4.71 ÷ 3 = _____

47. 5.28 ÷ 3 = _____

48. 0.56 ÷ 4 = _____

49. 0.75 ÷ 5 = _____

50. 5.82 ÷ 6 = _____

51. 8.61 ÷ 7 = _____

52. 5.28 ÷ 8 = _____

Divide. Round each quotient to the nearest tenth.

Example

$$
\begin{array}{r}
1.66 \\
3\overline{)5.00} \\
3 \\
\hline
20 \\
18 \\
\hline
20 \\
18 \\
\hline
2
\end{array}
$$

$5 \div 3$ is about 1.7.

53.

$$
3\overline{)2.}
$$

$2 \div 3$ is about _____.

54.

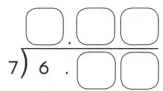

6 ÷ 7 is about _____.

55.

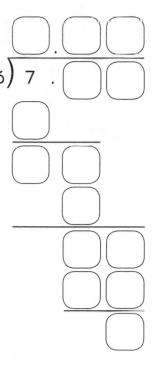

7 ÷ 6 is about _____.

Divide. Round each quotient to the nearest hundredth.

56.   5 ÷ 9

57.   8 ÷ 7

58.   11 ÷ 3

Worksheet 4   Dividing by Tens, Hundreds, or Thousands

Place the decimal point in the correct place in the quotient.

Example

$7.26 \div 10 = 0.7\,2\,6$

When you divide a number by 10, move the decimal point 1 decimal place to the left.

---

1. $1.37 \div 10 = 1\,3\,7$

2. $3.85 \div 10 = 3\,8\,5$

3. $36.2 \div 10 = 3\,6\,2$

4. $94.7 \div 10 = 9\,4\,7$

5. $645 \div 10 = 6\,4\,5$

6. $786 \div 10 = 7\,8\,6$

7. $0.9 \div 10 = \quad 9$

8. $0.4 \div 10 = \quad 4$

Complete.

9. $2.84 \div 10 = $ _____

10. $463 \div 10 = $ _____

11. $0.95 \div 10 = $ _____

12. $72.6 \div 10 = $ _____

Complete.

13. $57.8 \div $ _____ $= 5.78$

14. $4 \div $ _____ $= 0.4$

15. $894 \div $ _____ $= 89.4$

16. $0.26 \div $ _____ $= 0.026$

17.   _____ $\div 10 = 3.09$

18.   _____ $\div 10 = 70.4$

19.   _____ $\div 10 = 0.05$

20.   _____ $\div 10 = 0.458$

Complete.

21. $90 \div 30 = (90 \div$ _____$) \div 10$

22. $140 \div 20 = (140 \div$ _____$) \div 10$

23. $280 \div 40 = ($_____$\div 4) \div 10$

24. $420 \div 70 = ($_____$\div 7) \div 10$

Complete.

25. $60 \div 20 = (60 \div$ _____$) \div 10$

       $=$ _____ $\div 10$

       $=$ _____

26. $120 \div 30 = (120 \div$ _____$) \div 10$

       $=$ _____ $\div 10$

       $=$ _____

27. $360 \div 40 = ($_____$\div 4) \div 10$

       $=$ _____ $\div 10$

       $=$ _____

28. $560 \div 80 = ($_____$\div 8) \div 10$

       $=$ _____ $\div 10$

       $=$ _____

29. $16 \div 80 = ($ _____ $\div\ 8) \div 10$

   $= $ _____ $\div\ 10$

   $= $ _____

30. $21 \div 70 = ($ _____ $\div\ 7) \div 10$

   $= $ _____ $\div\ 10$

   $= $ _____

31. $0.9 \div 30 = ($ _____ $\div\ 3) \div 10$

   $= $ _____ $\div\ 10$

   $= $ _____

32. $0.15 \div 50 = ($ _____ $\div\ 5) \div 10$

   $= $ _____ $\div\ 10$

   $= $ _____

Divide.

33. $1.4 \div 70 = $ _____

34. $8 \div 40 = $ _____

35. $9 \div 30 = $ _____

36. $0.75 \div 50 = $ _____

37. $0.42 \div 70 = $ _____

Place the decimal point in the correct place in the quotient.

___ Example ___

$61.5 \div 100 = 0.6\ 1\ 5$

When you divide a number by 100, move the decimal point 2 decimal places to the left.

38. $23.8 \div 100 =\ 2\ 3\ 8$ **39.** $47.3 \div 100 =\ 4\ 7\ 3$

40. $37.5 \div 100 =\ \ 3\ 7\ 5$ **41.** $98.4 \div 100 =\ \ 9\ 8\ 4$

42. $5.9 \div 100 =\ \ 5\ 9$ **43.** $2.7 \div 100 =\ \ 2\ 7$

Place the decimal point in the correct place in the quotient.

___ Example ___

$715 \div 1,000 = 0.7\ 1\ 5$

When you divide a number by 1,000, move the decimal point 3 decimal places to the left.

44. $147 \div 1,000 =\ 1\ 4\ 7$ **45.** $258 \div 1,000 =\ 2\ 5\ 8$

46. $69 \div 1,000 =\ \ 6\ 9$ **47.** $38 \div 1,000 =\ \ 3\ 8$

48. $1,234 \div 1,000 =\ 1\ 2\ 3\ 4$ **49.** $6,101 \div 1,000 =\ 6\ 1\ 0\ 1$

Name: _____ **Date:** _____

Complete.

50. $36.9 \div$ _____ $= 0.369$ **51.** $4 \div$ _____ $= 0.004$

52. $78 \div$ _____ $= 0.078$ **53.** $49.6 \div$ _____ $= 0.496$

54. _____ $\div 100 = 4.08$ **55.** _____ $\div 100 = 2.05$

56. _____ $\div 1{,}000 = 0.007$ **57.** _____ $\div 1{,}000 = 0.852$

Complete.

58. $800 \div 200 = (800 \div$ _____ $) \div 100$

59. $1{,}500 \div 300 = (1{,}500 \div$ _____ $) \div 100$

60. $40 \div 800 = ($ _____ $\div 8) \div 100$

61. $6 \div 200 = ($ _____ $\div 2) \div 100$

62. $0.9 \div 300 = ($ _____ $\div 3) \div 100$

63. $600 \div 2{,}000 = (600 \div$ _____ $) \div 1{,}000$

64. $1{,}800 \div 3{,}000 = (1{,}800 \div$ _____ $) \div 1{,}000$

65. $180 \div 9{,}000 = ($ _____ $\div 9) \div 1{,}000$

66. $8 \div 2{,}000 = ($ _____ $\div 2) \div 1{,}000$

67. $0.8 \div 4{,}000 = ($ _____ $\div 4) \div 1{,}000$

Complete.

68. 40 ÷ 200 = _____

69. 60 ÷ 3,000 = _____

70. 320 ÷ 800 = _____

71. 810 ÷ 9,000 = _____

72. 12 ÷ 3,000 = _____

73. 25 ÷ 5,000 = _____

74. 5 ÷ 100 = _____

75. 8 ÷ 400 = _____

76. 0.4 ÷ 200 = _____

77. 9 ÷ 600 = _____

78. 6 ÷ 2,000 = _____

79. 40 ÷ 5,000 = _____

80. 70 ÷ 1,000 = _____

81. 600 ÷ 4,000 = _____

82. 1,400 ÷ 500 = _____

83. 7,500 ÷ 1,500 = _____

Worksheet 5   Estimating Decimals

Round each decimal to the nearest whole number. Fill in the blanks.

> **Example**
>
> 1.375 is about __1__.   3 tenths is __less than__ __5__ tenths.
>
> 1.375 ⟶ 1

1.   12.459 is about _____.   4 tenths is _____ _____ tenths.

12.459 ⟶ _____

2.   43.607 is about _____.   6 tenths is _____ _____ tenths.

43.607 ⟶ _____

3.   28.910 Is about _____.   9 tenths is _____ _____ tenths.

28.910 ⟶ _____

Round each number to the nearest tenth. Fill in the blanks.

> **Example**
>
> 2.483 is about __2.5__.   8 hundredths is __greater than__ __5__ hundredths.
>
> 2.483 ⟶ __2.5__

4.   6.341 is about _____.   4 hundredths is _____ _____ hundredths.

6.341 ⟶ _____

5.   17.251 is about _____.   5 hundredths is _____ _____ hundredths.

17.251 ⟶ _____

6.   39.908 is about _____. 0 hundredths is _____ _____ hundredths.

39.908 ⟶ _____

7.   18.472 is about _____. 7 hundredths is _____ _____ hundredths.

18.472 ⟶ _____

Round each number to the nearest hundredth. Fill in the blanks.

> *Example*
>
> 1.284 is about _1.28_. 4 thousandths is _less than_ _5_ thousandths.
>
> 1.284 ⟶ _1.28_

8.   16.016 is about _____. 6 thousandths is _____ _____ thousandths.

16.016 ⟶ _____

9.   24.005 is about _____. 5 thousandths _____ _____ thousandths.

24.005 ⟶ _____

10.   45.076 is about _____. 6 thousandths is _____ _____ thousandths.

45.076 ⟶ _____

Round each decimal to the nearest whole number. Then estimate the sum.

> *Example*
>
> 0.47 + 2.52 is about _3_.   0.47 ⟶ _0_; 2.52 ⟶ _3_
>
> 0 + 3 = _3_

11.   1.62 + 3.39 is about _____.   1.62 ⟶ _____; 3.39 ⟶ _____

_____ + _____ = _____

12.   4.53 + 0.82 is about _____.   4.53 → _____; 0.82 → _____

_____ + _____ = _____

13.   7.49 + 2.39 is about _____.   7.49 → _____; 2.39 → _____

_____ + _____ = _____

14.   18.57 + 9.98 is about _____.   18.57 → _____; 9.98 → _____

_____ + _____ = _____

15.   4.67 + 0.88 is about _____.   4.67 → _____; 0.88 → _____

_____ + _____ = _____

Round each number to the nearest tenth. Then estimate the sum or difference.

> **Example**
>
> 0.51 + 2.48 is about __3__.   0.51 → __0.5__; 2.48 → __2.5__
>
> __0.5__ + __2.5__ = __3__

16.   7.39 − 2.91 is about _____.   7.39 → _____; 2.91 → _____

_____ − _____ = _____

17.   0.87 + 1.49 is about _____.

18.   12.39 − 4.72 is about _____.

19.   18.59 − 9.66 is about _____.

20.   21.85 + 0.75 is about _____.

Round each decimal to the nearest whole number. Then estimate the product.

> *Example*
>
>   2.47 × 4 is about ___8___.   2.47 ⟶ ___2___
>
>   ___2___ × 4 = ___8___

21.   3.51 × 7 is about _____.   3.51 ⟶ _____

                                        _____ × _____ = _____

22.   12.07 × 8 is about _____.

23.   15.76 × 11 is about _____.

24.   18.32 × 12 is about _____.

25.   27.13 × 13 is about _____.

Name: _____ Date: _____

Round each decimal to the nearest tenth. Then estimate the product.

┌─ *Example* ───┐
│   │
│   3.45 × 4 is about ___14___.   3.45 ⟶ 3.5   │
│   │
│   __3.5__ × 4 = __14__ │
│   │
└──┘

26.   4.54 × 6 is about _____.   4.54 ⟶ _____

_____ × _____ = _____

27.   14.27 × 7 is about _____.

28.   16.94 × 9 is about _____.

Round each decimal to the nearest whole number. Then estimate the quotient.

┌─ *Example* ───┐
│   │
│   12.49 ÷ 4 is about ___3___.   12.49 ⟶ __12__   │
│   │
│   __12__ ÷ 4 = __3__ │
│   │
└──┘

29.   31.52 ÷ 8 is about _____.   31.52 ⟶ _____

_____ ÷ _____ = _____

30.   71.63 ÷ 9 is about _____.

31.   62.55 ÷ 7 is about _____.

Estimate. Round the decimals to the nearest tenth.

> *Example*
>
> 12.77 ÷ 4 is about ___3.2___.   12.77 ⟶ ___12.8___
>
>   ___12.8___ ÷ 4 = ___3.2___

32.   37.24 ÷ 6 is about _____.   37.24 ⟶ _____

                                            _____ ÷ _____ = _____

33.   21.64 ÷ 8 is about _____.

34.   51.09 ÷ 7 is about _____.

Worksheet 6   Converting Metric Units

Find each product.

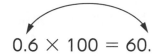

> **Example**
>
> $$0.6 \times 100 = 60.$$
>
> When you multiply a decimal by 100, move the decimal point 2 decimal places to the right.

1. $0.08 \times 100 =$ _____

2. $0.09 \times 100 =$ _____

3. $0.015 \times 100 =$ _____

4. $0.047 \times 100 =$ _____

5. $7.9 \times 100 =$ _____

6. $12.34 \times 100 =$ _____

Convert meters to centimeters.

7. $0.4 \text{ m} = 0.4 \times$ _____

      $=$ _____ cm

8. $7.43 \text{ m} = 7.43 \times$ _____

      $=$ _____ cm

9. $1.585 \text{ m} =$ _____ $\times$ _____

      $=$ _____ cm

10. $500.75 \text{ m} =$ _____ $\times$ _____

      $=$ _____ cm

Convert meters to meters and centimeters.

> *Example*
>
> 14.05 m
>
> Express this part as meters.   Express this part as centimeters.
>
> 14 ⟶ __14__ m   0.05 m = 0.05 × 100
>
> 14.05 m = __14__ m __5__ cm   = __5__ cm

11.   15.09 m

0.09 m = 0.09 × _____

= _____ cm

15.09 m = _____ m _____ cm

12.   224.8 m

0.8 m = 0.8 × _____

= _____ cm

224.8 m = _____ m _____ cm

13.   35.09 m = _____ m _____ cm

14.   158.6 m = _____ m _____ cm

Find each product.

> **Example**
>
> $0.75 \times 1{,}000 = 750.$
>
>
> When you multiply a decimal by 1,000, move the decimal point 3 decimal places to the right.

15. $0.04 \times 1{,}000 = $ _____

16. $0.07 \times 1{,}000 = $ _____

17. $0.026 \times 1{,}000 = $ _____

18. $0.038 \times 1{,}000 = $ _____

19. $6.2 \times 1{,}000 = $ _____

20. $45.67 \times 1{,}000 = $ _____

Convert kilometers to meters.

21. $0.6 \text{ km} = 0.6 \times$ _____

= _____ m

22. $8.32 \text{ km} = 8.32 \times$ _____

= _____ m

23. $1.493 \text{ km} = $ _____ $\times$ _____

= _____ m

24. $300.92 \text{ km} = $ _____ $\times$ _____

= _____ m

Convert kilograms to grams.

25.   7.04 kg = 7.04 × _____

   = _____ g

26.   25.8 kg = 25.8 × _____

   = _____ g

27.   9.05 kg = 9.05 × _____

   = _____ g

28.   14.2 kg = 14.2 × _____

   = _____ g

Convert liters to milliliters.

29.   5.08 L = 5.08 × _____

   = _____ mL

30.   14.3 L = 14.3 × _____

   = _____ mL

31.   3.07 L = _____ × _____

   = _____ mL

32.   26.4 L = _____ × _____

   = _____ mL

Convert kilometers to kilometers and meters.

Example

28.75 km

Express this part as kilometers.

28 → ___28___ km

28.75 m = ___28___ km ___750___ m

Express this part as meters.

0.75 m = 0.75 × 1,000

= ___750___ m

---

33. 46.07 km

0.07 km = 0.07 × _____

= _____ m

46.07 km = _____ km _____ m

34. 168.9 km

_____ km = _____ × _____

= _____ m

168.9 km = _____ km _____ m

35. 57.04 km = _____ km _____ m

36. 248.5 km = _____ km _____ m

Convert kilograms to kilograms and grams.

Example

4.78 kg

Express this part as kilograms.   Express this part as grams.

4 kg ⟶ ____4____ kg   0.78 kg = 0.78 × 1,000

4.78 kg = ____4____ kg __780__ g   = __780__ g

37.   2.05 kg

0.05 kg = 0.05 × _____

= _____ g

2.05 kg = _____ kg _____ g

38.   12.9 kg

0.9 kg = _____ × _____

= _____ g

12.9 kg = _____ kg _____ g

39.   9.03 kg = _____ kg _____ g

40.   21.6 kg = _____ kg _____ g

Convert liters to liters and milliliters.

```
┌─ Example ──────────────────────────────────────────────────────┐
│                                                                 │
│                           5.67 L                                │
│                          ↗     ↖                                │
│   Express this part as liters.        Express this part as milliliters. │
│                                                                 │
│   5 L →  ___5___ L              0.67 L = 0.67 × 1,000           │
│                                                                 │
│                                       =  ___670___ mL          │
│                                                                 │
│                                                                 │
│   5.67 mL = ___5___ L ___670___ mL                             │
│                                                                 │
└─────────────────────────────────────────────────────────────────┘
```

41. 8.03 L

0.03 L = 0.03 × _____

= _____ mL

8.03 L = _____ L _____ mL

42. 24.7 L

0.7 L = _____ × _____

= _____ mL

24.7 L = _____ L _____ mL

43. 7.01 L = _____ L _____ mL

44. 15.8 L = _____ L _____ mL

Convert centimeters to meters.

Example

Convert 17.5 centimeters to meters.

100 cm = 1 m

17.5 cm = 17.5 ÷ 100

= ____0.175____ m

When you divide a number by 100, move the decimal point 2 decimal places to the left.

---

45.   25.4 cm = 25.4 ÷ _____

= _____ m

46.   9.83 cm = 9.83 ÷ _____

= _____ m

47.   32.5 cm = 32.5 ÷ _____

= _____ m

48.   127.6 cm = 127.6 ÷ _____

= _____ m

Name: _____ **Date:** _____

Convert meters and centimeters to meters.

> *Example*
>
> 48 m 70 cm
>
> 100 cm = 1 m
>
> 70 cm = 70 ÷ 100
>
> = ____0.7____ m
>
> 48 m 70 cm = ____48.7____ m
>
> When you divide a number by 100, move the decimal point 2 decimal places to the left.

49. 29 m 40 cm

40 cm = _____ ÷ _____

= _____ m

29 m 40 cm = _____ m

50. 15 m 80 cm

80 cm = _____ ÷ _____

= _____ m

15 m 80 cm = _____ m

51. 26 m 90 cm = _____ m

52. 145 m 30 cm = _____ m

Convert meters to kilometers.

> *Example*
>
> Convert 7,845 meters to kilometers.
>
> 1,000 m = 1 km
>
> 7,845 m = 7,845 ÷ 1,000
>
> = __7.845__ km

When you divide a number by 1,000, move the decimal point 3 decimal places to the right.

53. 4,970 m = 4,970 ÷ _____

= _____ km

54. 2,587 m = _____ km

55. 12,783 m = _____ km

Convert grams to kilograms.

> *Example*
>
> Convert 7,250 grams to kilograms.
>
> 1,000 g = 1 kg
>
> 7,250 g = 7,250 ÷ 1,000
>
> = __7.250__ kg

When you divide a number by 1,000, move the decimal point 3 decimal places to the left.

56. 826 g = 826 ÷ _____

= _____ kg

57. 4,458 g = _____ kg

58. 997 g = _____ kg

Convert milliliters to liters.

─ Example ─

Convert 1,275 milliliters to liters.

1,000 mL = 1 L

1,275 mL = 1,275 ÷ 1,000

= __1.275__ L

When you divide a number by 1,000, move the decimal point 3 decimal places to the left.

59. 773 mL = 773 ÷ _____

= _____ L

60. 335 mL = _____ L

61. 4,785 mL = _____ L

Convert kilometers and meters to kilometers.

Example

7 km 25 m

1,000 m = 1 km

25 m = 25 ÷ 1,000

$\quad$ = _0.025_ km

7 km 25 m = 7 km + _0.025_ km

$\quad$ = _7.025_ km

> When you divide a number by 1,000, move the decimal point 3 decimal places to the left.

62. 5 km 8 m

8 m = 8 ÷ _____

$\quad$ = _____ km

5 km 8 m = 5 km + _____ km

$\quad$ = _____ km

63. 32 km 74 m = _____ km

64. 66 km 9 m = _____ km

Convert kilograms and grams to kilograms.

> **Example**
>
> 470 kg 800 g
>
> 800 g = 800 ÷ 1,000
>
> = ___0.8___ kg
>
> 470 kg 800 g = 470 kg + ___0.8___ kg
>
> = ___470.8___ kg

> When you divide a number by 1,000, move the decimal point 3 decimal places to the left.

65. 75 kg 600 g

600 g − 600 ÷ _____

= _____ kg

75 kg 600 g = _____ kg + _____ kg

= _____ kg

66. 66 kg 90 g = _____ kg

67. 175 kg 175 g = _____ kg

Convert liters and milliliters to liters.

─── *Example* ───────────────────────────────

55 L 450 mL

450 mL = 450 ÷ 1,000

        = __0.45__ L

55 L 450 mL = 55 L + __0.45__ L

           = __55.45__ L

When you divide a number by 1,000, move the decimal point 3 decimal places to the left.

68. 124 L 900 mL

900 mL = 900 ÷ _____

      = _____ L

124 L 900 mL = _____ L + _____ L

            = _____ L

69. 78 L 45 mL = _____ L

70. 255 L 750 mL = _____ L

Solve. Show your work.

71.   James planted 2 trees 750 meters apart. He planted 12 trees in total.

    a.   Find the distance between the first and the twelfth tree in meters.

    b.   Express the distance between them in kilometers.

72.   Trader A sells 5 bags of rice. Each bag weighs 45 kilograms 650 grams each. A truck can only carry 3,850 kilograms of goods. What is the maximum number of bags of rice that the truck can carry?

73. It requires 15 bottles of water to fill 1 container. One bottle contains 800 milliliters of water. Lisa buys 12 containers. Find the total volume of water that the containers carry. Express the answer in liters.

74. Gerald will need 2 meters 50 centimeters of cloth to make a shirt. What is the total length of cloth he needs to buy to make 22 shirts? Express the answer in meters.

Worksheet 7   Real-World Problems: Decimals

Solve. Show you work.

1. The length of a cracker is 3.2 centimeters. John places 4 crackers in a row. Estimate the total length of 1 row of crackers.

    3.2 cm ⟶ _____ cm

    _____ ✕ _____ = _____ cm

    The total length is about _____ centimeters.

2. Rose joins 6 pieces of ribbon. Each piece of ribbon is 7.57 centimeters long. Estimate the total length of the 6 pieces of ribbon.

    The total length is about _____ centimeters.

3.   Kim has $78.65. She distributes her money equally among her six children. Estimate the amount of money each child gets.

$78.65 \longrightarrow 6 \times$ _____ $=$ _____ $6 \times$ _____ $=$ _____

$6 \times$ _____ $=$ _____

_____ is nearer to 78.

Since $6 \times$ _____ $= 78$, each child gets about $_____.

4.   Brad has a rope that is 65 meters long. He wants to cut the rope into 4 equal parts. Find the length of each cut part to the nearest meter.

Hint: Think of a number that when multiplied by 4 is close to 65.

$65 \longrightarrow 4 \times$ _____ $=$ _____ $4 \times$ _____ $=$ _____

$4 \times$ _____ $=$ _____

_____ is nearer to 65.

Since $4 \times$ _____ $=$ _____, the length of each cut part of the rope is

about _____ meters.

5. Jennifer has $15 with her. She wants to buy the following items to bake a loaf of banana bread: a bag of flour for $2.65, a carton of eggs for $1.89, a bag of nuts for $4.57, and a bunch of bananas for $1.66. Does Jennifer have enough money to buy all four items?

6. The capacity of a pail is 2.17 liters. Ethan fills 9 of these pails with water in order to fill a larger bucket. Find the capacity of the larger bucket. Round your answer to the nearest liter.

7.   Tom drove 15.67 miles from home to Paddle Middle School to get his brother, Alex. They stopped for a lemonade at a café that is 8.92 miles from home. What is the distance between the café and the school?
Round your answer to the nearest mile.

8.   Shane is training for the National Vertical Marathon. His best time so far is 9.33 minutes. Shane wants to complete the marathon in 7.5 minutes. How much time must Shane shave off his best time to achieve his goal?
Round your answer to the nearest minute.

A vertical marathon is a competition where one has to try to run up many flights of stairs (usually in a tall building) and complete it in as short a time as possible.

CHAPTER 10 Percent

Worksheet 1   Percent

Each 10 × 10 grid has some shaded parts. Fill in the blanks to describe each grid.

Example

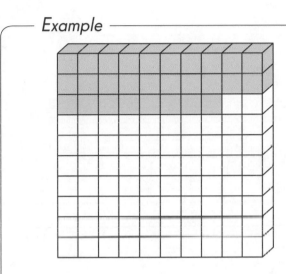

_____28_____ out of 100 parts are shaded.

_____28_____% of the whole is shaded.

_____72_____ out of 100 parts are **not** shaded.

_____72_____% of the whole is **not** shaded.

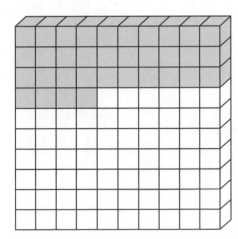

1.   _____ out of 100 parts are shaded.

2.   _____% of the whole is shaded.

3.   _____ out of 100 parts are **not** shaded.

4.   _____% of the whole is **not** shaded.

Express each fraction as a percent.

— *Example* —

$$\frac{74}{100} = \underline{74}\%$$

5. $\dfrac{18}{100} = \underline{}\%$

6. $\dfrac{55}{100} = \underline{}\%$

7. $\dfrac{63}{100} = \underline{}\%$

Express each fraction as a percent.

— *Example* —

$$\frac{3}{10} = \frac{\boxed{30}}{100}$$

$$= \underline{30}\%$$

8. $\dfrac{9}{10} = \dfrac{\boxed{}}{100}$

$$= \underline{}\%$$

9. $\dfrac{7}{10} = \dfrac{\boxed{}}{100}$

$$= \underline{}\%$$

10. $\dfrac{8}{10} = \dfrac{\boxed{}}{100}$

$$= \underline{}\%$$

Express each decimal as a percent.

Example

$$0.24 = \frac{\boxed{24}}{100}$$

$$= \underline{\quad 24 \quad}\%$$

11. $0.4 = \dfrac{\boxed{}}{100}$

$= \underline{\hspace{2cm}}\%$

12. $0.79 = \dfrac{\boxed{}}{100}$

$= \underline{\hspace{2cm}}\%$

13. $0.46 = \dfrac{\boxed{}}{100}$

$= \underline{\hspace{2cm}}\%$

14. $0.01 = \dfrac{\boxed{}}{100}$

$= \underline{\hspace{2cm}}\%$

15. $0.08 = \dfrac{\boxed{}}{100}$

$= \underline{\hspace{2cm}}\%$

16. $0.09 = \dfrac{\boxed{}}{100}$

$= \underline{\hspace{2cm}}\%$

Express each percent as a fraction.

┌─ *Example* ───┐

$27\% = \dfrac{27}{100}$

└───┘

17. $21\% = \dfrac{\boxed{}}{\boxed{}}$ **18.** $63\% = \dfrac{\boxed{}}{\boxed{}}$

19. $9\% = \dfrac{\boxed{}}{\boxed{}}$ **20.** $3\% = \dfrac{\boxed{}}{\boxed{}}$

Express each percent as a decimal.

┌─ *Example* ───┐

$18\% = \dfrac{18}{100} = \underline{\quad 0.18 \quad}$

└───┘

21. $37\% = \dfrac{\boxed{}}{100} = \underline{\qquad\qquad}$

22. $94\% = \dfrac{\boxed{}}{100} = \underline{\qquad\qquad}$

23. $5\% = \dfrac{\boxed{}}{100} = \underline{\qquad\qquad}$

24. $9\% = \dfrac{\boxed{}}{100} = \underline{\qquad\qquad}$

Express each fraction in simplest form.

25. $\dfrac{36}{100} = \dfrac{\boxed{}}{\boxed{}}$

26. $\dfrac{15}{100} = \dfrac{\boxed{}}{\boxed{}}$

27. $\dfrac{72}{100} = \dfrac{\boxed{}}{\boxed{}}$

28. $\dfrac{18}{100} = \dfrac{\boxed{}}{\boxed{}}$

Express each percent as a fraction in simplest form.

Example

$$20\% = \dfrac{\boxed{20}}{100}$$

$$= \underline{\ \ \frac{1}{5}\ \ }$$

29. $42\% = \dfrac{\boxed{}}{100}$

$= \underline{\hspace{2cm}}$

30. $75\% = \dfrac{\boxed{}}{100}$

$= \underline{\hspace{2cm}}$

31. $8\% = \dfrac{\boxed{}}{100}$

$= \underline{\hspace{2cm}}$

32. $5\% = \dfrac{\boxed{}}{100}$

$= \underline{\hspace{3cm}}$

Express each item as a percent, and then as a decimal.

		Percent	Decimal
33.	7 out of 100		
34.	4 out of 10		
35.	9 out of 10		

Express each item as a decimal, and then as a fraction.

		Decimal	Fraction
36.	0%		
37.	8%		
38.	33%		
39.	74%		
40.	100%		

Express each item as a percent, and then as a fraction.

		Percent	Fraction
41.	0		
42.	0.7		
43.	0.44		
44.	0.73		
45.	1		

Fill in the blanks.

46. Samantha had $100. She spent $45 on a meal.

Money spent = _____%

Money left = _____%

47. A tank contained 10 liters of water. Alvin poured out some water from the tank and there were 3 liters of water left.

Water left = _____%

Water used = _____%

48. Of the 100 children who visited the zoo, 35 are girls.

What percent of the children are girls? _____%

What percent of the children are boys? _____%

49. Of the 100 books borrowed by students, 76 are English books.

What percent of the books are English books? _____%

What percent of the books are not English books? _____%

Solve.

50. What percent of the fruits are pears?

Complete the model with the words *Fruits* and *Pears*.

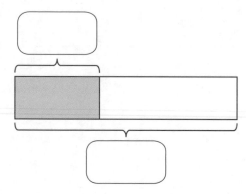

51. What percent of the visitors are adults?

Complete the model with the words *Visitors* and *Adults*.

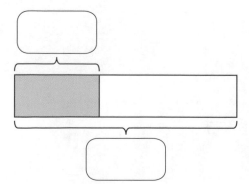

Name: _____ Date: _____

Worksheet 2   Expressing Fractions as Percents

Express each fraction as a percent.

> *Example*
>
> $$\frac{23}{50} = \frac{\boxed{46}}{100}$$
>
> $$= \underline{\quad 46 \quad}\%$$

1. $\frac{11}{20} = \frac{\boxed{}}{100}$

   $= \underline{\qquad}\%$

2. $\frac{47}{50} = \frac{\boxed{}}{100}$

   $= \underline{\qquad}\%$

3. $\frac{3}{5} = \frac{\boxed{}}{100}$

   $= \underline{\qquad}\%$

4. $\frac{3}{4} = \frac{\boxed{}}{100}$

   $= \underline{\qquad}\%$

5. $\frac{17}{25} = \frac{\boxed{}}{100}$

   $= \underline{\qquad}\%$

Express each fraction as a percent.

Example

$$\frac{7}{25} = \frac{\frac{7}{25}}{\underline{\hspace{2cm}}} \times \underline{\hspace{1cm}1\hspace{1cm}}$$

$$= \frac{\frac{7}{25}}{\underline{\hspace{2cm}}} \times \underline{\hspace{1cm}100\hspace{1cm}}\%$$

$$= \underline{\hspace{1cm}28\hspace{1cm}}\%$$

6. $\frac{31}{50} = \underline{\hspace{2cm}} \times \underline{\hspace{2cm}}$

$\hspace{1.2cm} = \underline{\hspace{2cm}} \times \underline{\hspace{2cm}}\%$

$\hspace{1.2cm} = \underline{\hspace{2cm}}\%$

7. $\frac{9}{20} = \underline{\hspace{2cm}} \times \underline{\hspace{2cm}}$

$\hspace{1.2cm} = \underline{\hspace{2cm}} \times \underline{\hspace{2cm}}\%$

$\hspace{1.2cm} = \underline{\hspace{2cm}}\%$

Express each fraction as a percent.

Example

$$\frac{66}{300} = \frac{\boxed{22}}{100} = \underline{\hspace{1cm}22\hspace{1cm}}\%$$

8. $\frac{44}{200} = \frac{\boxed{}}{100} = \underline{\hspace{2cm}}\%$

9. $\frac{68}{400} = \frac{\boxed{}}{100} = \underline{\hspace{2cm}}\%$

10. $\dfrac{125}{500} = \dfrac{\boxed{}}{100} = $ _____ %

11. $\dfrac{424}{800} = \dfrac{\boxed{}}{100} = $ _____ %

Express each fraction as a percent.

Example

$\dfrac{3}{10}$

10 parts $\longrightarrow$ 100%

1 part $\longrightarrow$ _____10_____ %

3 parts $\longrightarrow$ _____30_____ %

$\dfrac{3}{10} = $ _____30_____ %

---

12. $\dfrac{13}{20}$

20 parts $\longrightarrow$ 100%

1 part $\longrightarrow$ _____ %

13 parts $\longrightarrow$ _____ %

$\dfrac{13}{20} = $ _____ %

13. $\dfrac{9}{25}$

25 parts $\longrightarrow$ 100%

1 part $\longrightarrow$ _____ %

9 parts $\longrightarrow$ _____ %

$\dfrac{9}{25} = $ _____ %

Solve.

14. Sam completed $\frac{7}{25}$ of his homework.

What percent of his homework is not completed?

25 units ⟶ 100%

1 unit ⟶ _____%

7 units ⟶ _____%

Homework completed = _____%

Homework not completed = _____%

15. Kenneth did $\frac{4}{5}$ of his homework.

a. What percent of his homework did Kenneth do?

b. What percent of his homework was left undone?

16. Last year, $\frac{18}{25}$ of Ahmad's land was planted with mango trees. The rest of the land was planted with orange trees. What percent of Ahmad's land was planted with orange trees?

17. Olivia planned to hike the full length of a new trail in one afternoon. Olivia walked $\frac{1}{4}$ of the trail. She cycled for $\frac{1}{5}$ of the trail. What percent of the trail did Olivia not complete?

Fraction of the trail completed = _____ + _____

= _____

_____ units ⟶ 100%

1 unit ⟶ _____%

_____ units ⟶ _____%

Fraction of the trail not completed = _____ − _____

= _____

Percent of the trail not completed = _____%

18. Rob had a basket of fruit. Of the fruit, $\frac{1}{3}$ were apples and $\frac{5}{12}$ were oranges. The rest were pears. What percent of the fruit was pears?

19. Serena gave $\frac{1}{2}$ of her pizza to Tina and $\frac{1}{4}$ to Andrew. What percent of the pizza was left?

Worksheet 3   Percent of a Number

Find each answer.

Example

$100\% \longrightarrow 50$

$1\% \longrightarrow \dfrac{50}{100} = 0.5$

$30\% \longrightarrow \underline{0.5 \times 30 = 15}$

---

1. $100\% \longrightarrow 30$

$1\% \blacktriangleright$ _____

$50\% \longrightarrow$ _____

2. $100\% \longrightarrow 40$

$1\% \longrightarrow$ _____

$60\% \longrightarrow$ _____

Example

25% of 280

$= \underline{\quad \dfrac{25}{100} \quad} \times \underline{\quad 280 \quad}$

$= \underline{\quad 70 \quad}$

---

3.   70% of 150

$= \underline{\qquad} \times \underline{\qquad}$

$= \underline{\qquad}$

4.   45% of 320

$= \underline{\qquad} \times \underline{\qquad}$

$= \underline{\qquad}$

Solve these problems using two methods.

5. There were 480 penguin eggs in a basket. Yesterday, 40% of the eggs hatched. How many eggs hatched?

Method 1:

40% of 480 eggs = _____ × _____

= _____

_____ eggs hatched.

Method 2:

100% ⟶ _____ eggs

1% ⟶ _____ eggs

_____% ⟶ _____ eggs

_____ eggs hatched.

6. Mrs. Smith had $850. She spent 60% of it on gifts for her children. How much did Mrs. Smith spend on the gifts?

Method 1:

Method 2:

7. A butcher bought 240 kilograms of meat. He sold 15% of the meat and kept the rest in a refrigerator.

    a. What percent of the meat was kept in the refrigerator?

        _____% − _____% = _____%

        _____% of the meat was kept in the refrigerator.

    b. How many kilograms of meat were kept in the refrigerator?

    Method 1:

        _____% × 240 kg = _____ × 240 kg

                    = _____ kg

        _____ kilograms of meat were kept in the refrigerator.

    Method 2:

        100% ⟶ _____

          1% ⟶ _____

        _____% ⟶ _____

        _____ kilograms of meat were kept in the refrigerator.

Solve. Show your work.

8. There were 800 students in a school. 55% of the students in the school were Caucasian and 22% were African American. The rest were Hispanic.

   a. What percent of the students were Hispanic?

   b. How many students were Hispanic?

9.   Mr. Anderson's monthly salary was $2,000. He spent 45% of his salary on food, 42% of it on rent, and saved the rest. How much money did Mr. Anderson save?

Worksheet 4   Real-World Problems: Percent

Solve. Show your work.

Example

Joleen has $15,000 in a savings account at Booming Bank. The **interest** rate for the account is 6% per year. Home Mart is offering a 20% storewide **discount**. Joleen is deciding whether or not to buy a furniture set. The regular price of the furniture set at Home Mart is $4,700. There is a 7% **sales tax** on the sale price of the furniture set.

a. How much interest will Joleen earn after 1 year (assuming she makes no withdrawals)?

6% of $15,000

$= \dfrac{6}{100} \times \$15,000$

$= \$900$

She will earn $900 in interest after 1 year.

b. How much sales tax would she pay on the furniture set?

20% of $4,700

$= \dfrac{20}{100} \times \$4,700$

$= \$940$

The dollar amount of the discount is $940.

$4,700 - \$940 = \$3,760$

7% of $3,760

$= \dfrac{7}{100} \times \$3,760$

$= \$263.20$

She would pay $263.20 sales tax.

Name: _____ Date: _____

1. Mr. Taylor puts $1,600 in Value Bank. The interest rate is 4% per year. How much interest will he get after 1 year?

2. Ms. Benjamin puts $1,200 in Virtue bank. The interest rate is 6% per year.

a. How much interest will she get after one year?

b. How much money will Ms. Benjamin have in the bank after one year?

3. Benny bought a DVD recorder for $800. He had to pay 5% sales tax
on the DVD recorder. How much sales tax did Benny pay?

4. The price of a computer was $1,500. Lisa bought the computer and had
to pay 5% sales tax on the price.

   a. How much sales tax did Lisa pay?

   b. How much did she pay in total?

5. The regular price of a refrigerator was $1,200. Ms. Williams bought the refrigerator at a discount of 15%. How much was the discount?

6. At a sale, Mrs. Jones bought a piano at a discount of 20%. The regular price of the piano was $4,200.

   a. What was the discounted price for the piano?

   b. Mrs. Jones paid 5% sales tax on the sale price. How much sales tax did she pay?

CHAPTER 11 Graphs and Probability

Worksheet 1   Making and Interpreting Line Plots

Complete.

1. $2 \times \frac{1}{8} + 3 \times \frac{1}{4} = $ _____

2. $4 \times \frac{1}{2} + 5 \times \frac{3}{4} = $ _____

3.   The weight of a bag of nuts is $\frac{3}{4}$ pound. Lisa bought 12 bags of nuts. What is the total weight of the nuts she bought?

4.   Sam bought some nuts that came in 1-pound bags. He gave each of his 3 friends $\frac{2}{5}$ pound of nuts. There were some nuts left over, so he gave each friend another $\frac{2}{5}$ pound. He continued until he had given out all the nuts he bought. What is the minimum number of 1-pound bags that Sam could have bought?

Name: ____________________ Date: ____________

Complete.

Emma has two types of butter. She has 5 sticks of butter X, weighing $\frac{1}{4}$ pound each. She has 3 sticks of butter Y, weighing $\frac{3}{4}$ pound each.

5. Create a table and a line plot to show the two types of butter.

	Butter X	Butter Y
Weight (lb)		
Number of Sticks		

Emma's Butter by Weight

Sue has several bottles of four kinds of bottled juice. Each of the three bottles of Juice A has a volume of $\frac{1}{4}$ quart. The only bottle of Juice B has a volume of $\frac{1}{2}$ quart. Each of the two bottles of Juice C has a volume of $\frac{3}{8}$ quart. Each of the four bottles of Juice D has a volume of $\frac{3}{4}$ quart.

6.   Draw a table and a line plot to show the four kinds of juice.

	Juice A	**Juice B**	**Juice C**	**Juice D**
Volume of Bottles (qt)				
Number of Bottles				

Sue's Juice by Volume

7.   How many bottles are there altogether?

8.   What is the total volume of Juice A?

9.   What is the total volume of Juice D?

10.   What is the total volume of all four kinds of juice?

11.   If the juice is mixed together and then divided equally among all the bottles, what is the volume of juice in each bottle?

The table shows the four types of packaged meat that Sam sold in one day.

	Chicken	Beef	Pork	Turkey
Weight per Package (lb)	$\frac{1}{4}$	$\frac{1}{8}$	$\frac{1}{2}$	$\frac{5}{8}$
Number of Packages	5	3	2	4

12. How many packages of meat are there altogether?

13. What is the total weight of beef sold?

14. What is the total weight of chicken sold?

15. What is the total weight of meat sold?

16. If all the turkey and chicken are mixed and repacked equally into 8 packages, what is the weight of each package?

Worksheet 2 Making and Interpreting Double Bar Graphs

Use the data in the table to draw a bar graph and answer the questions.

Example

The table shows the types of tickets sold at a school fair.

	10¢	20¢	50¢	$1	$2
Total number of tickets	50	70	200	150	80

Draw a bar graph to show the different types of tickets sold.

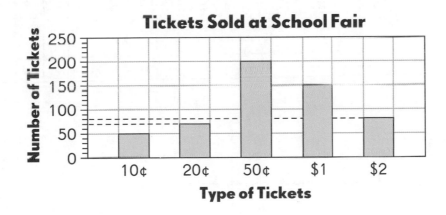

Which ticket is the most popular? _____50¢_____

Which ticket is the least popular? _____10¢_____

How many more $1 tickets than $2 tickets were sold? _____70_____

How many tickets were sold in all? _____550_____

Name: _____ Date: _____

The table shows the number of points scored by students Amy, Ben, Carrie, Danny, Eva, and Flora.

	Amy	Ben	Carrie	Danny	Eva	Flora
Score	7	9	12	6	3	1

Draw a bar graph to show the points scored by each student.

Points Scored by Students

1. Who scored the most points? _____

2. Who scored the fewest points? _____

3. How many more points did Danny score than Flora? _____

4. Who scored three times as many points as Eva? _____

5. How many more points must Amy score so that she gets as many points as Carrie? _____

6. How many more points must Eva score so that she gets one point fewer than Ben? _____

Use the data in the table to draw a double bar graph and answer the questions.

Example

The table shows the different kinds of toppings that children picked for their yogurt at Jazz Café.

	Chocolate		Vanilla		Strawberry		Butterscotch	
	Boys	Girls	Boys	Girls	Boys	Girls	Boys	Girls
Number	15	12	10	14	8	10	8	6

Draw a **double bar graph** to show the different kinds of toppings picked by the boys and girls for their yogurt.

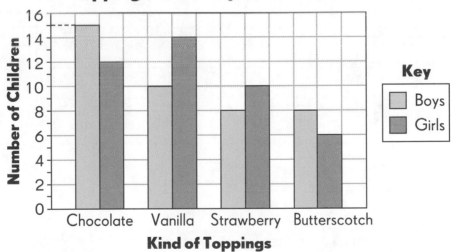

Toppings Picked by the Children

Which topping is the children's favorite? _____Chocolate_____

Which topping is the least popular? _____Butterscotch_____

How many more children chose the chocolate topping than the

butterscotch topping? _____13_____

How many children chose the strawberry topping? _____18_____

The table shows the favorite sports of all the students in a school.

	Soccer		Baseball		Football	
	Boys	Girls	Boys	Girls	Boys	Girls
Number	16	22	24	22	16	8

Draw a double bar graph to show the favorite sports of the boys and girls in the school.

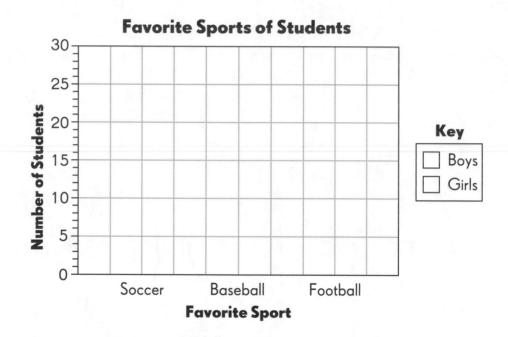

7.   How many girls like soccer? _____

8.   Do more students prefer baseball or soccer? _____

How many more? _____

9.   Which is the most popular sport? _____

10.   Which is the least popular sport? _____

11. How many girls are there in the school? _____

12. How many boys are there in the school? _____

The table shows the fruit Chris and Larry picked at a farm.

	Apples		Oranges		Pears	
	Chris	Larry	Chris	Larry	Chris	Larry
Pieces	80	100	75	45	90	60

Draw a double bar graph.

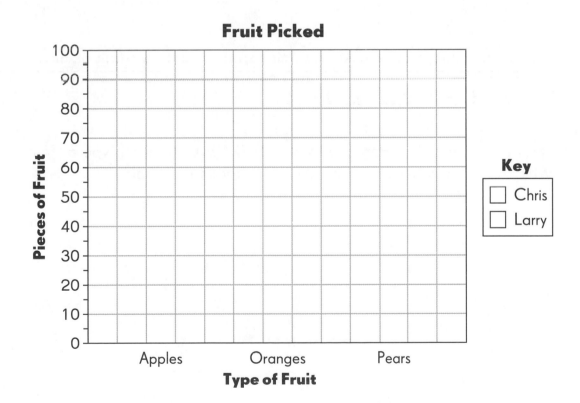

13. How many pieces of fruit did Chris pick? _____

14. Who picked more fruit, Chris or Larry? _____

How many more? _____

15. Which type of fruit do Chris and Larry have the most of?

Chris: _____; Larry: _____

16. Which type of fruit do they have the least of? _____

17. How many more oranges must Chris pick so that he has twice as many

oranges as Larry? _____

18. How many more apples must Larry pick so that Chris has half as many

apples as Larry? _____

19. The boys' goal is for each one to pick 100 pieces of each type of fruit.
Which boy has to pick the most pieces to reach the goal?

20. Explain two ways to find the answer for **19**.

Worksheet 3   Graphing an Equation

Write the ordered pair for each point.

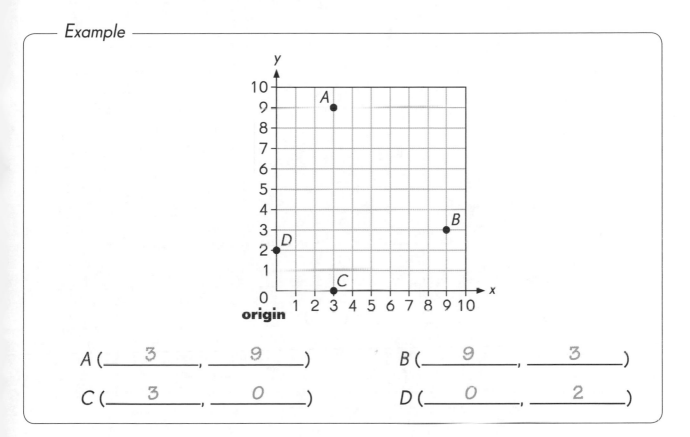

— *Example* —

A (___3___, ___9___)   B (___9___, ___3___)

C (___3___, ___0___)   D (___0___, ___2___)

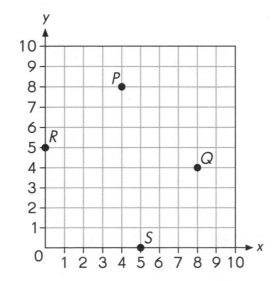

1.   P (_____, _____)   **2.**   Q (_____, _____)

3.   R (_____, _____)   **4.**   S (_____, _____)

Plot each point on the coordinate grid.

— *Example* —

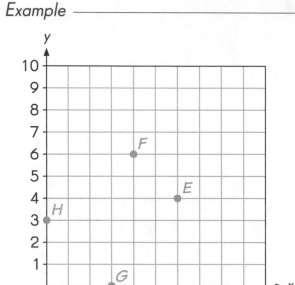

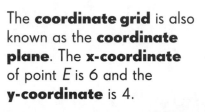

The **coordinate grid** is also known as the **coordinate plane**. The **x-coordinate** of point *E* is 6 and the **y-coordinate** is 4.

E (6, 4)   F (4, 6)

G (3, 0)   H (0, 3)

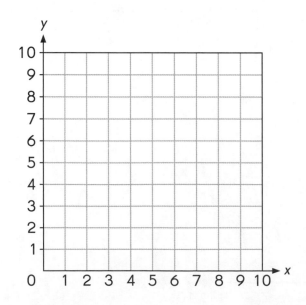

5.   *W* (0, 7)   **6.**   *T* (3, 5)

7.   *U* (5, 3)   **8.**   *V* (7, 0)

Use the data in the table to plot the graph and answer the questions.

Mandy needs flavored syrup to make drinks for her party guests. The table shows the number of bottles of syrup needed for the number of guests at a party.

Number of Bottles of Syrup	1	2	3	4	5
Number of Guests	8	16	24	32	40

9. How many bottles of syrup does Mandy need when there are

24 guests? _____

10. How many bottles of syrup does she need when a total of 30 guests

are at the party? _____

11.   Mandy used 2.5 bottles of syrup for a party she held last month.

How many guests were there? _____

12.   Mandy has 1.5 bottles of syrup left. How many guests can she invite

to her next party? _____

13.   Mandy invited 20 guests to a party. Later that night, 15 more uninvited

guests arrived. How many more bottles of syrup does she need? _____

Worksheet 4   Comparing Data Using Line Graphs

Use the data in the tables to plot the graph and complete the exercises.

1.   Complete the tables using the equations $y = 4x$ and $y = 7x$.

y = 4x

x	1	2	3	4	5
y					

y = 7x

x	1	2	3	4	5
y					

2.   Plot the ordered pairs on the coordinate grid below. Then draw the two lines.

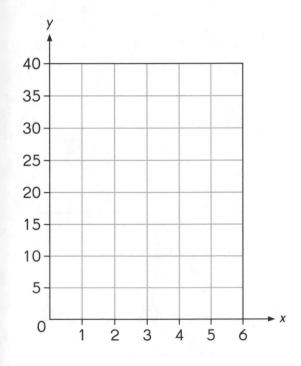

3.   Find the values of y when x = 4.

4.   Find the values of x when y = 20.

5.   Find the difference in the values of y when the value of x is 7.

Use the data in the table to plot the graph and answer the questions.

The table shows two children's savings over five weeks.

	Week 1	Week 2	Week 3	Week 4	Week 5
Jacob	$6	$12	$18	$24	$30
Sarah	$8	$16	$24	$32	$40

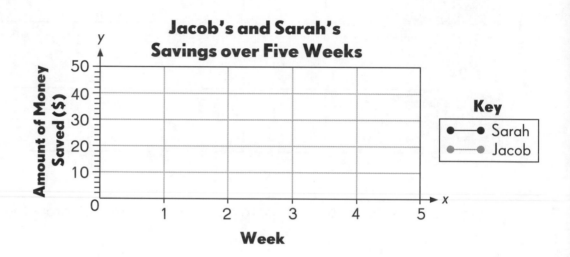

6. In which week were Jacob's savings $6 less than Sarah's savings?

_____

7. How much more were Sarah's savings than Jacob's savings after four weeks?

$_____

8. How much did Jacob and Sarah earn in all after five weeks? $_____

9. If Jacob and Sarah saved the same amount of money in Week 6 as they did in the previous weeks, how much would their savings be in Week 6?

Jacob's savings: $_____; Sarah's savings: $_____

10. After Week 5, Sarah bought her brother a birthday gift worth half her savings. Who has a greater amount in his or her savings now? By how much?

$_____; $_____

Worksheet 5   Combinations

Complete.

Example

Joanne has a black blazer, a brown blazer, and a gray blazer.
She has a beige skirt, a tan skirt, and a black skirt.
Make an **organized list** of the possible **combinations** of a blazer
and skirt that Joanne can wear.
Draw a **tree diagram** to show the number of combinations.

Blazer	Skirt	Combinations
Black	Beige	Black/Beige
Black	Tan	Black/Tan
Black	Black	Black/Black
Brown	Beige	Brown/Beige
Brown	Tan	Brown/Tan
Brown	Black	Brown/Black
Gray	Beige	Gray/Beige
Gray	Tan	Gray/Tan
Gray	Black	Gray/Black

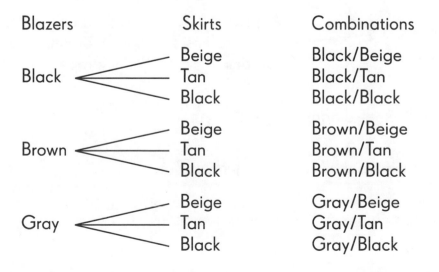

Blazers	Skirts	Combinations
Black	Beige	Black/Beige
	Tan	Black/Tan
	Black	Black/Black
Brown	Beige	Brown/Beige
	Tan	Brown/Tan
	Black	Brown/Black
Gray	Beige	Gray/Beige
	Tan	Gray/Tan
	Black	Gray/Black

1. Jack has a pair of red socks, a pair of black socks, and a pair of green socks. He has one blue tie and one brown tie. Make an organized list of the possible combinations of a tie and a pair of socks.

Socks	Ties	Combinations

There are _____ combinations.

2. Kim eats yogurt and fruit every day in different combinations.

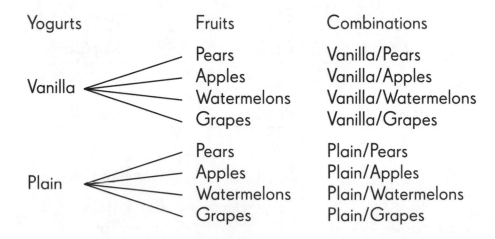

Yogurts	Fruits	Combinations
Vanilla	Pears	Vanilla/Pears
	Apples	Vanilla/Apples
	Watermelons	Vanilla/Watermelons
	Grapes	Vanilla/Grapes
Plain	Pears	Plain/Pears
	Apples	Plain/Apples
	Watermelons	Plain/Watermelons
	Grapes	Plain/Grapes

Study the tree diagram above.

How many types of fruit does Kim eat? _____

How many types of yogurt does she eat? _____

3.   Jill drinks either coffee or tea after a meal. She can choose to have cheese, biscuits, or fruit to go with her drink.

　　a.   Draw a tree diagram to show the number of combinations that she can have.

　　b.   How many combinations are there in all?

4. XYZ supermarket sells 4 choices of cheese, 5 choices of milk, and 6 choices of crackers.

a. There are _____ combinations of choosing one type of cheese and one type of milk.

b. There are _____ combinations of choosing one type of milk and one type of crackers.

c. There are _____ combinations of choosing one type of cheese and one type of crackers.

Worksheet 6   Theoretical Probability and Experimental Probability

Complete.

Example

Sandra makes a spinner.

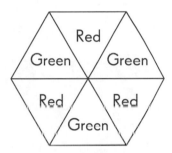

What is the theoretical and the experimental probability of an event happening?

Theoretical probability $= \dfrac{\text{number of favorable outcomes}}{\text{total number of possible outcomes}}$

Experimental probability $= \dfrac{\text{number of \textbf{favorable outcomes}} \text{ in an actual experiment}}{\text{total number of trials}}$

Find the theoretical probability of landing on the red section if the spinner is spun once.

Theoretical probability of landing on the red section $= \dfrac{3}{6} = \dfrac{1}{2}$

Jamal tosses two coins. The coins land on either a head or a tail.
(H, T) shows a head on the first coin and a tail on the second coin.

1.   Write down all possible outcomes. How many outcomes are there in all?

2.   What is the theoretical probability of landing a head and a tail?

3.   What is the theoretical probability of landing two heads?

4.   What is the theoretical probability of landing two tails?

Jess tosses a coin and a cube that is numbered 1 through 6 on its faces.
(H, 5) shows a head on the coin and a 5 on the cube.

5.   Write down all possible outcomes. How many outcomes are there in all?

6.   What is the theoretical probability of getting a head and an even number?

7.   What is the theoretical probability of getting a tail and a number less than 5?

8.   What is the theoretical probability of getting a head and a number greater than 3?

Sarah tosses a coin 100 times and she gets a head 45 times and a tail 55 times.

9.   Find the experimental probability of getting a head.

10.   Find the experimental probability of getting a tail.

11.   Jenny and Trish throw a cube that is numbered 1 through 6 on its faces.
The cube is thrown 45 times by each girl. Use the data in the table to find
the experimental probability of each girl getting each number. Complete the
table.

Number	Jenny's Outcomes	Experimental Probability	Trish's Outcomes	Experimental Probability
1	8		7	
2	9		8	
3	8		8	
4	6		7	
5	5		6	
6	9		9	

12. Harris makes a spinner that has 4 equal parts. Two parts are painted red, one part is painted green, and one part is painted yellow. He spins the spinner a number of times and obtains these experimental probabilities.

Red 0.52   Green 0.25   Yellow 0.23

What could be the total number of times he spins the spinner?
There is more than one correct answer.
Using your total number of spins, find the number of times the spinner lands on each color.

Angles

Worksheet 1   Angles on a Line

Solve.

Example

The **sum of angle measures** on a **line** is 180°.

a. Name the **angles** on line *PR*.
Is $\overrightarrow{QX}$ **perpendicular** to $\overleftrightarrow{PR}$?

b. Name the **angles** on line *AC*.
Is $\overrightarrow{BD}$ **perpendicular** to $\overleftrightarrow{AC}$?

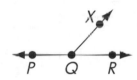 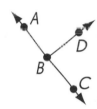

a. $\angle PQX$ and $\angle XQR$
$\overrightarrow{QX}$ is not perpendicular to $\overleftrightarrow{PR}$ as m$\angle PQX$ is not equal to 90°.

b. $\angle ABD$ and $\angle DBC$
$\overrightarrow{BD}$ is perpendicular to $\overleftrightarrow{AC}$ as m$\angle ABD = 90°$.

---

1. Study the figure on the right and find the line.
Check your answer by using a protractor.
Then add up the angle measures on the line.

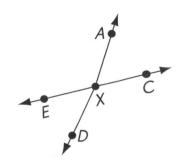

_____ is a line because

m$\angle$_____ + m$\angle$_____ = 180°.

Measure ∠*a* using a protractor. Find the measure of ∠*b*.

┌─ *Example* ──────────────────────────────────────┐

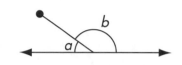

m∠a + m∠b = 180°

m∠a = _____35°_____

m∠b

= 180° − m∠a

= 180° − _____35°_____

= _____145°_____

└──┘

2.

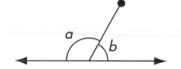

m∠a + m∠b = 180°

m∠a = _____

m∠b

= 180° − _____

= _____

3.

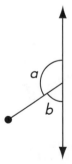

m∠a + m∠b = 180°

m∠a = _____

m∠b

= _____ − _____

= _____

Name: _____ **Date:** _____

$\overleftrightarrow{AB}$ **is a line. Find the measure of each unknown angle.**

4.

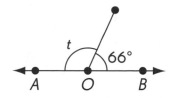

m∠t

= _____ − 66°

= _____

5.

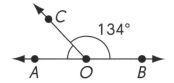

m∠AOC

= _____ − _____

= _____

∠**ABC is a right angle. Measure** ∠x **using a protractor. Find the measure of** ∠y.

6.

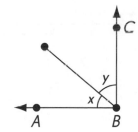

m∠x + m∠y − 90°

m∠x = _____

m∠y = 90° − m∠x

= 90° − _____

= _____

7.

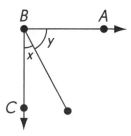

m∠x + m∠y = 90°

m∠x = _____

m∠y = 90° − m∠x

= 90° − _____

= _____

$\overrightarrow{AB}$ is perpendicular to $\overrightarrow{BC}$. Find the measure of each unknown angle.

8.

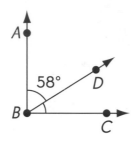

$m\angle DBC$

$=$ _____ $-$ _____

$=$ _____

9.

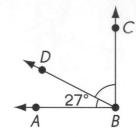

$m\angle CBD$

$=$ _____ $-$ _____

$=$ _____

$\overleftrightarrow{AB}$ is perpendicular to $\overrightarrow{CD}$. Find the measure of each unknown angle.

10.

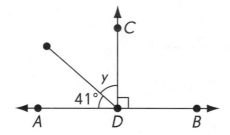

$m\angle y + 41° + 90° = 180°$

$m\angle y +$ _____ $= 180°$

$m\angle y =$ _____ $-$ _____

$=$ _____

11.

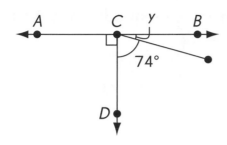

$m\angle y + 74° + 90° = 180°$

$m\angle y + $ _____ $= 180°$

$m\angle y = $ _____ $-$ _____

$= $ _____

12. $\overleftrightarrow{AB}$ is a line. ADC is a right angle. Find the measure of $\angle x$.

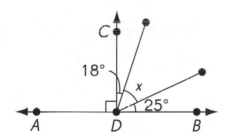

Complete.

13. $\overleftrightarrow{AC}$ is a line. Find the measure of $\angle x$.

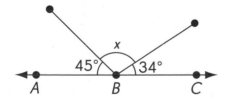

14.   Circle the cards which contain the angle measures that add up to 180°.

115°

47°   28°

37°   98°

44°

Worksheet 2   Angles at a Point

Complete.
Name the angles at point *O* and state the sum of the measures of the angles.

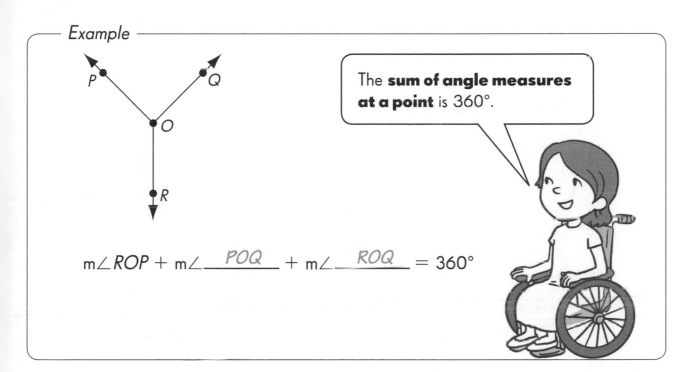

Example

The **sum of angle measures at a point** is 360°.

$$m\angle ROP + m\angle \underline{\quad POQ \quad} + m\angle \underline{\quad ROQ \quad} = 360°$$

1.

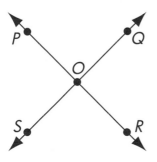

$$m\angle \underline{\quad\quad} + m\angle \underline{\quad\quad} + m\angle \underline{\quad\quad} + m\angle \underline{\quad\quad} = 360°$$

Find the measure of the unknown angles using a protractor and state the sum of the measures of the angles.

Example

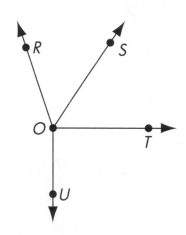

m∠SOT + m∠TOU + m∠SOR + m∠ROU

= _____55°_____ + _____90°_____ + _____54°_____ + _____161°_____

= _____360°_____

2.

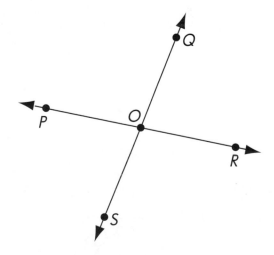

m∠POQ + m∠QOR + m∠ROS + m∠SOP

= _____ + _____ + _____ + _____

= _____

Find the measure of ∠s using a protractor. Find the measure of ∠t.

3.

m∠s + m∠t = 360°

m∠s = _____

m∠t = 360° − m∠s

= 360° − _____

= _____

4.

m∠s + m∠t = 360°

m∠s = _____

m∠t = 360° − m∠s

= 360° − _____

= _____

Find the measure of the unknown angle.

5.

m∠x

= _____ − 115°

= _____

6.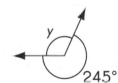

m∠y

= _____ − _____

= _____

Complete.

7. $\overleftrightarrow{AB}$ and $\overleftrightarrow{CD}$ are lines. Find the measures of ∠x, ∠y, and ∠z.

8.   Find the measure of ∠x.

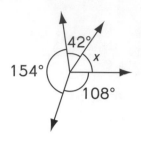

9. $\overleftrightarrow{AC}$ is a line. Find the measure of ∠x.

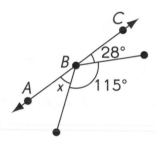

10.   Circle the cards which contain the angle measures that add up to 360°.

70°

180°   145°

85°   220°

130°

Worksheet 3   Vertical Angles

Complete.

> *Example*
>
> $\overleftrightarrow{PR}$ and $\overleftrightarrow{SQ}$ are **intersecting lines**.
> Name the pairs of vertical angles.
>
>
>
> **Vertical angles** have equal measures.
>
> $m\angle\underline{\quad POQ \quad} = m\angle\underline{\quad SOR \quad}$
>
> $m\angle\underline{\quad POS \quad} = m\angle\underline{\quad QOR \quad}$

1.   *ABCD* is a square.
Name the pairs of vertical angles.

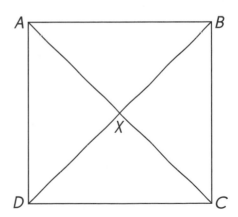

$m\angle\underline{\qquad\qquad} = m\angle\underline{\qquad\qquad}$

$m\angle\underline{\qquad\qquad} = m\angle\underline{\qquad\qquad}$

2. $m\angle p = m\angle r$
$m\angle q = m\angle s$
Use the above statements to help you name the angles in the diagram.
Give two possible answers.

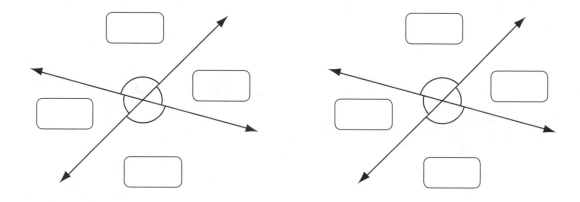

3.

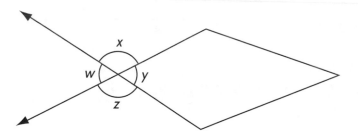

Look at the diagram above. Name the marked angles that are vertical angles.

$m\angle$_____ $= m\angle$_____

$m\angle$_____ $= m\angle$_____

4. $\overleftrightarrow{WY}$ and $\overleftrightarrow{XZ}$ are lines.
Find the measures of $\angle YOZ$ and $\angle WOX$.

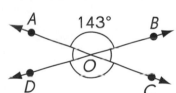

m$\angle YOZ$ = _____

m$\angle WOX$ = _____

5. $\overleftrightarrow{AC}$ and $\overleftrightarrow{BD}$ are lines.
Find the measures of $\angle AOD$, $\angle COD$, and $\angle BOC$.

m$\angle AOD$ = _____

m$\angle COD$ = _____

m$\angle BOC$ = _____

6.   Find the measure of ∠x.

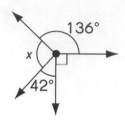

7. $\overleftrightarrow{AB}$ and $\overleftrightarrow{CD}$ are lines. Find the measure of ∠x.

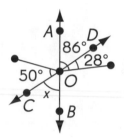

8. $\overleftrightarrow{PS}$, $\overleftrightarrow{QT}$, and $\overleftrightarrow{RV}$ are lines.
        Find the measures of ∠UOV, ∠TOU, and ∠SOT.

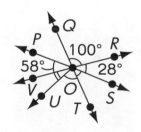

Properties of Triangles and Four-Sided Figures

Worksheet 1   Classifying Triangles

The figures are not drawn to scale.

Write *true* or *false* for each statement.

Triangle *ABC* is an equilateral triangle.

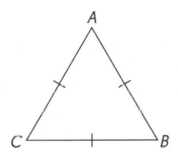

1. Any two sides are equal. _____

2. All the angles measure 60°. _____

3. A right triangle can also be an equilateral triangle. _____

4. An equilateral triangle can also be an isosceles triangle. _____

5. An isosceles triangle can never be an equilateral triangle. _____

Put a check in the box if the triangle is an equilateral triangle.

6.
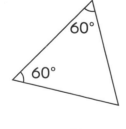

7.
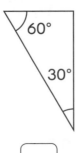

8.
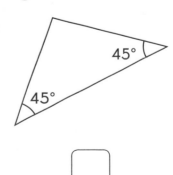

Write *true* or *false* for each statement.

Triangle *PQR* is an isosceles triangle.

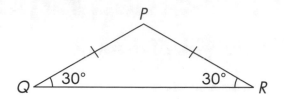

9. Two sides are equal. _____

10. Any two angles are equal. _____

11. A triangle with three equal sides can also be an isosceles triangle. _____

12. A right triangle can also be an isosceles triangle. _____

Put a check in the box if the triangle is an isosceles triangle.

13. 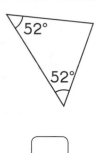   **14.** 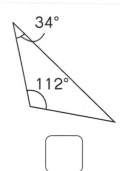   **15.**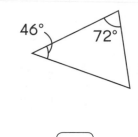

Write *true* or *false* for each statement.

Triangle *WXY* is a scalene triangle.

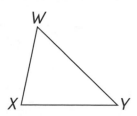

16. All three sides are of different lengths. _____

17. All three angle measures are different. _____

Put a check in the box if the triangle is a scalene triangle.

18.

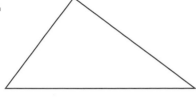

☐

19.

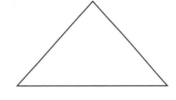

☐

20.

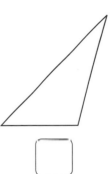

☐

Write *true* or *false* for each statement.

Triangle *ABC* is a right triangle.

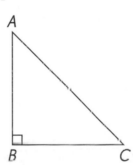

21.   One angle is 90°.   _____

22.   The sum of any two angle measures is 90°.   _____

23.   The sum of all the angle measures is 90°.   _____

Put a check in the box if the triangle is a right triangle.

24.

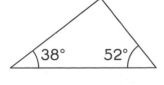

☐

25.

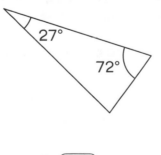

☐

26.

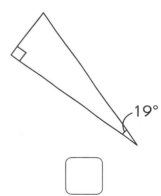

☐

Write _true_ or _false_ for each statement.

Triangle _STU_ is an obtuse triangle.

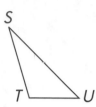

27.   All the angles measure less than 90°.   _____

28.   An obtuse triangle can also be an isosceles or a scalene triangle.   _____

Put a check in the box if the triangle is an obtuse triangle.

29.   **30.**      **31.**

Write _true_ or _false_ for each statement.

Triangle _PQR_ is an acute triangle.

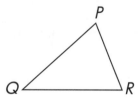

32.   All the angles measure greater than 90°.   _____

33.   An acute triangle can also be an equilateral, isosceles, or scalene triangle.   _____

Put a check in the box if the triangle is an acute triangle.

34.   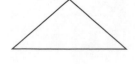   **35.**   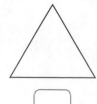   **36.**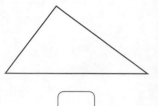

Worksheet 2   Measures of Angles of a Triangle

The figures are not drawn to scale.

Write *true* or *false* for each statement.

Triangle *XYZ* has three unequal sides.

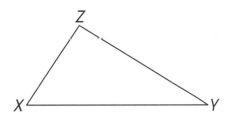

1. $\angle X$, $\angle Y$, and $\angle Z$ are the three angles of the triangle.   _____

2.   The sum of the measures of $\angle X$, $\angle Y$, and $\angle Z$ is 180°.   _____

3.   All the angles must measure less than 90°.   _____

4.   At most one angle measure is equal to or greater than 90°.   _____

Complete. Find the unknown angle measures.

┌─ *Example* ───┐

A

78°

26° C

B

$m\angle B = $ ____76°____

└───┘

Name: _____   Date: _____

5.

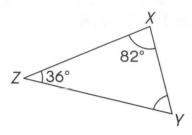

$m\angle Y =$ _____

6.

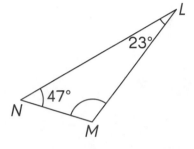

$m\angle M =$ _____

7.

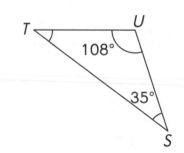

$m\angle T =$ _____

8. $\overline{PR}$ is a line segment. Find the measure of $\angle PQS$.

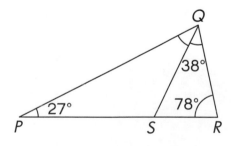

9. $\overline{AC}$ is a line segment. Find the measure of $\angle BDC$.

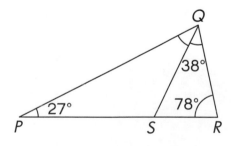

10. *ABC* is a right triangle.

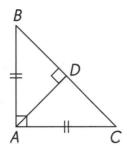

a. Find the measure of ∠*C*.

b. $\overline{AD}$ is perpendicular to $\overline{BC}$ at *D*. Find the measure of ∠*DAC*.

Complete.

11.

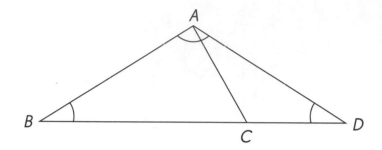

$$m\angle\underline{\hspace{1.5cm}} + m\angle\underline{\hspace{1.5cm}} + m\angle\underline{\hspace{1.5cm}} = 180°$$

Write *true* or *false* for each statement.

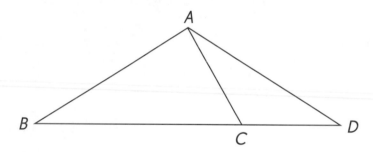

12. $m\angle ABC + m\angle BAC + m\angle BCA = 90°$ _____

13. $m\angle ADC + m\angle DAC + m\angle BAC + m\angle ABC = 180°$ _____

14. $m\angle ADC + m\angle DAC + m\angle ACD = 180°$ _____

Use the figure below to complete Exercises 15 to 18.

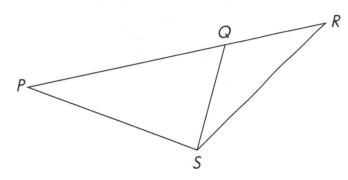

Write 3 sets of angles that total 180°.

15. | m∠ | | m∠ | | m∠ |

16. | m∠ | | m∠ | | m∠ |

17. | m∠ | | m∠ | | m∠ |

Write a set of 4 angles that total 180°.

18. | m∠ | | m∠ | | m∠ | | m∠ |

Triangle *ABC* is not drawn to scale.

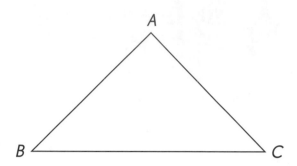

Write *true* or *false* for each statement.

19. If $m\angle B + m\angle C = 90°$, then $m\angle A$ is 90°. _____

20. If $m\angle A = 90°$, then $m\angle B$ is less than 90°. _____

Write 3 different possible measures for $\angle B$ and $\angle C$.

21. If $m\angle A = 80°$, then $m\angle B =$ _____ $m\angle C =$ _____

22. If $m\angle A = 80°$, then $m\angle B =$ _____ $m\angle C =$ _____

23. If $m\angle A = 80°$, then $m\angle B =$ _____ $m\angle C =$ _____

Worksheet 3   Right, Isosceles, and Equilateral Triangles

Find the unknown angle measure in each right triangle.

Example

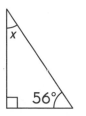

This is a **right triangle**.

m∠x = _____34_____°

1.

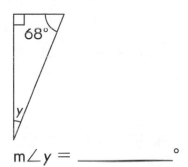

m∠y = _____°

2.

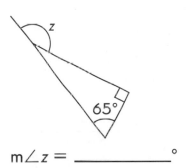

m∠z = _____°

Find the unknown angle measure in each isosceles triangle.

Example

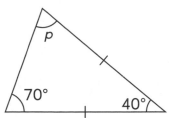

This is an **isosceles triangle**.

m∠p = _____70_____°

3.

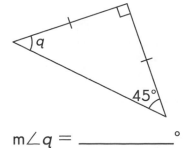

m∠q = _____°

4.

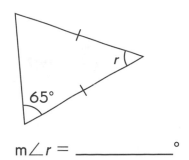

m∠r = _____°

Name: _____   **Date:** _____

Find the unknown angle measure(s) in each isosceles triangle.

Example

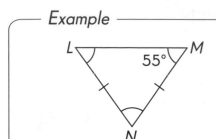

$m\angle MLN =$ _____55_____ °

$m\angle LNM =$ _____70_____ °

5.

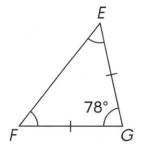

$m\angle FEG =$ _____ °

$m\angle EFG =$ _____ °

6. $\overrightarrow{PS}$ is a ray.

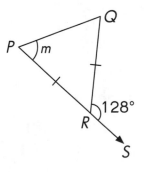

$m\angle m =$ _____ °

7. $\overrightarrow{AC}$ is a ray.

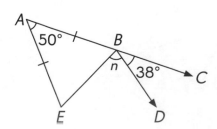

$m\angle n =$ _____ °

8. *ABC* is an isosceles triangle with sides *AB* = *AC*.

    a. m∠*A* = 70°
        Find the measure of ∠*C*.

    b. Point *D* is on segment *BC*. $\overline{AD}$ is perpendicular to $\overline{BC}$.
        Find the measure of ∠*DAC*.

9. *ABC* is an isosceles triangle with sides *AB* = *AC*.

    a. m∠*A* = 105°
        Find the measure of ∠*C*.

    b. Point *D* is on segment *BC*.
        m∠*DAC* = 25°
        Find the measure of ∠*ADB*.

Find the unknown angle measure(s).

Example

This is an **equilateral triangle**.

m∠*a* = 60°

10.

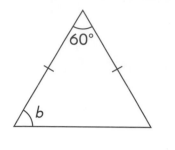

_____

11.

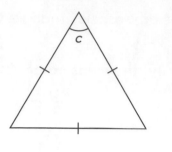

_____

12.

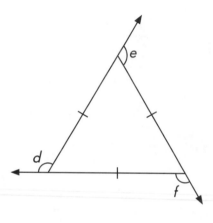

_____

13.

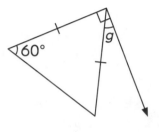

_____

14.

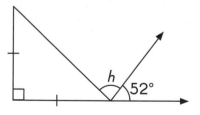

_____

15.

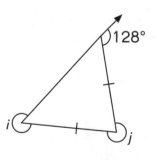

_____

16.

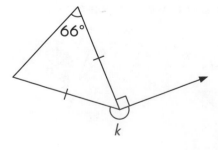

_____

17.

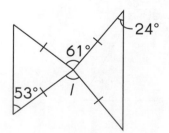

_____

Worksheet 4   Triangle Inequalities

The figure is not drawn to scale.

Example

Complete.

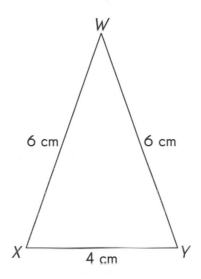

$WX =$ _____6_____ cm $XY =$ _____4_____ cm

$WY =$ _____6_____ cm $WX + XY =$ _____10_____ cm

$XY + WY =$ _____10_____ cm $WX + WY =$ _____12_____ cm

Look at the triangle *WXY*. Fill in the blanks with *Yes* or *No*.

Is $WX + XY > WY$? _____Yes_____

Is $XY + WY > WX$? _____Yes_____

Is $WX + WY > XY$? _____Yes_____

These are **inequalities**.

**The figure is not drawn to scale.
Complete.**

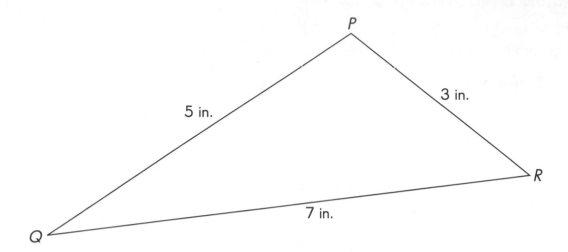

1. $PQ =$ _____ in.

2. $QR =$ _____ in.

3. $PR =$ _____ in.

4. $PQ + QR =$ _____ in.

5. $QR + PR =$ _____ in.

6. $PQ + PR =$ _____ in.

Look at the triangle _PQR_. Fill in the blanks with _Yes_ or _No_.

7.   Is $PQ + QR > PR$? _____

8.   Is $QR + PR > PQ$? _____

9.   Is $PQ + PR > QR$? _____

Show whether it is possible to form triangles with these sides.

10. 2 in., 3 in., 5 in.

11. 4 cm, 5 cm, 10 cm

12. 6 cm, 7 cm, 8 cm

Find all the possible lengths for the missing side. The lengths are in whole centimeters or whole inches.

Example

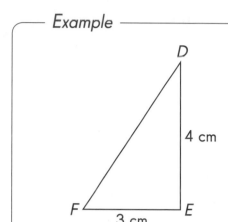

D

4 cm

F ——— E
3 cm

DF is greater than 4 centimeters.

What are the possible lengths of $\overline{DF}$?

$DE + EF = 4 \text{ cm} + 3 \text{ cm}$
$\qquad\qquad = 7 \text{ cm}$
$DE + EF > DF$
$7 \text{ cm} > DF$

So, *DF* is greater than 4 centimeters and less than 7 centimeters. The possible lengths of *DF* are 5 centimeters and 6 centimeters.

---

13. In triangle *ABC*, *AB* = 5 inches, *BC* = 6 inches, and *AC* is greater than 4 inches. What are the possible lengths of $\overline{AC}$?

14. *XYZ* is a triangle in which *XY* = 11 centimeters and *YZ* = 15 centimeters. The length of *XZ* is in whole centimeters and is greater than 20 centimeters. What are the possible lengths of $\overline{XZ}$?

Worksheet 5   Parallelogram, Rhombus, and Trapezoid

The figures are not drawn to scale.

Write *true* or *false* for each statement.

The figure is a parallelogram.

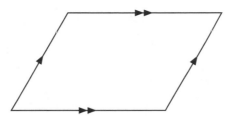

1. All sides are of equal length. _____

2. All angle measures are equal. _____

3. Opposite sides of the parallelogram are of equal length. _____

4. The measures of the opposite angles of the parallelogram are equal. _____

Put a check in the box if the figure is a parallelogram.

5.

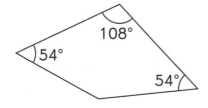

6.

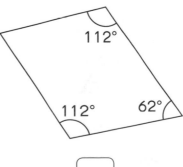

Find the unknown angle measure(s) in each parallelogram.

┌─ *Example* ───┐

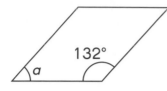

132°
a

This is a **parallelogram**.
The opposite sides are
parallel.

$\underline{m\angle a = 180° - 132°}$

$\underline{\quad = 48°\quad}$

└──┘

7.

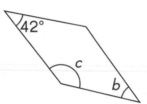

_____

_____

8.

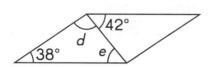

_____

_____

9.

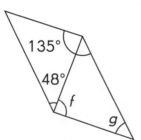

_____

_____

10.

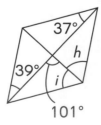

_____

_____

Name: _____ **Date:** _____

Write *true* or *false* for each statement.

The figure is a rhombus.

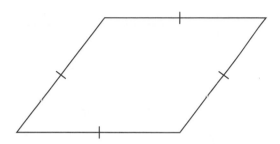

11.   All the sides of a rhombus are of equal length.   _____

12.   All the angle measures of a rhombus are equal.   _____

13.   Opposite sides of a rhombus are of equal length.   _____

14.   The measures of the opposite angles of a rhombus are equal.   _____

15.   A rhombus is also a parallelogram.   _____

Put a check in the box if the figure is a rhombus.

16.

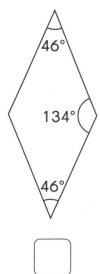

17.

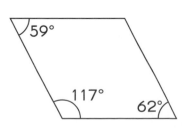

Name: _____ Date: _____

Find the unknown angle measure(s) in each rhombus.

Example

$m\angle a = 180° - 148°$

$= 32°$

A **rhombus** is a special kind of parallelogram.

18.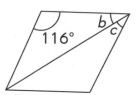

_____

_____

19.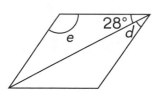

_____

_____

20.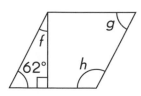

_____

_____

21.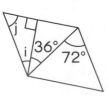

_____

_____

Write *true* or *false* for each statement.

The figure is a trapezoid.

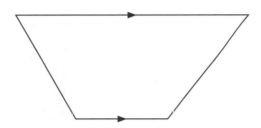

22.   All the sides of a trapezoid are of equal length.   _____

23.   All the angle measures of a trapezoid are equal.   _____

24.   A trapezoid has only one pair of opposite sides of
       equal length.   _____

25.   A trapezoid has only one pair of opposite angles of
       equal measure.   _____

26.   A trapezoid is also a parallelogram.   _____

Put a check in the box if the figure is a trapeziod.

27.   28.

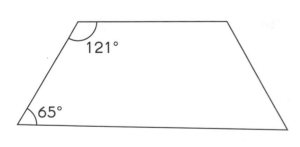

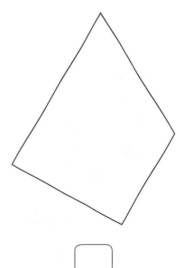

Name: _____   **Date:** _____

Find the unknown angle measure(s) in each trapezoid.

Example

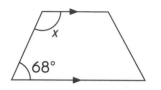

This is a **trapezoid**. One pair of opposite sides is parallel.

$m\angle x +$ ___68°___ $= 180°$

$m\angle x =$ ___180°___ $-$ ___68°___

$=$ ___112°___

29.

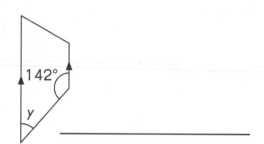

_____

30.

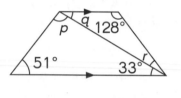

_____

31.

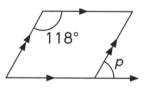

_____

32.

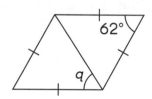

_____

33.

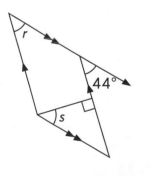

_____

34.

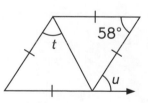

_____

35.

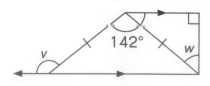

_____

CHAPTER 14 Surface Area and Volume

Worksheet 1 Building Solids Using Unit Cubes

How many unit cubes are used to build each solid?

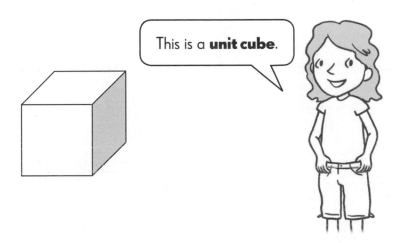

This is a **unit cube**.

1.

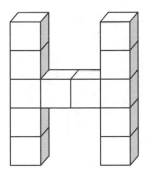

_____ unit cubes

2.

_____ unit cubes

3.

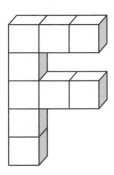

_____ unit cubes

4.

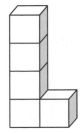

_____ unit cubes

5.

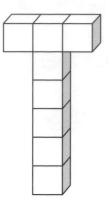

_____ unit cubes

6.

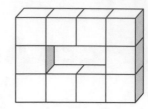

_____ unit cubes

7.

_____ unit cubes

8.

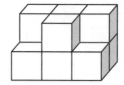

_____ unit cubes

9.

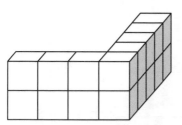

_____ unit cubes

10.

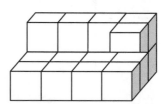

_____ unit cubes

Worksheet 2   Drawing Cubes and Rectangular Prisms

Draw these cubes or rectangular prisms on the dot paper without showing the unit cubes.

Example

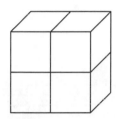

1.

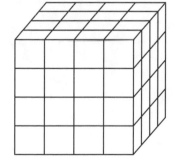

2.

3.

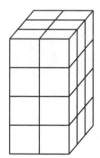

4.

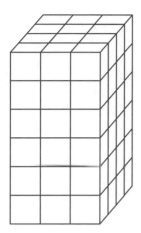

Complete the drawing of each cube or rectangular prism.

5.

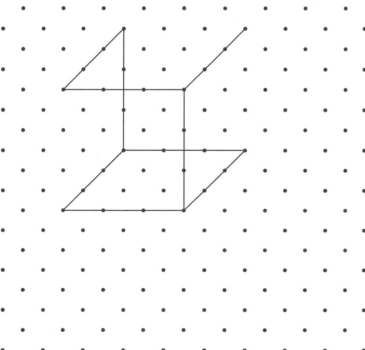

6.

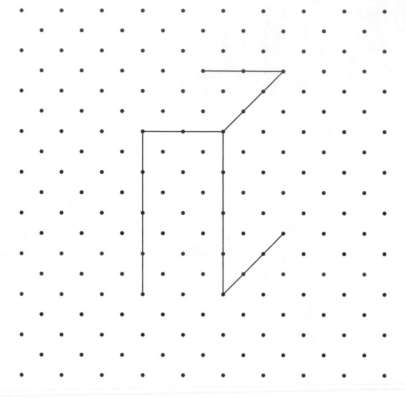

Draw a rectangular prism that has edges 3 times as long as this prism.

7.

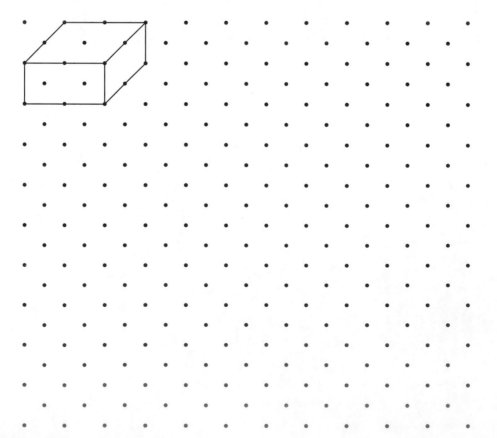

Worksheet 3   Prisms and Pyramids

Complete.

Example

In the figures, circle two vertices and shade two faces gray.

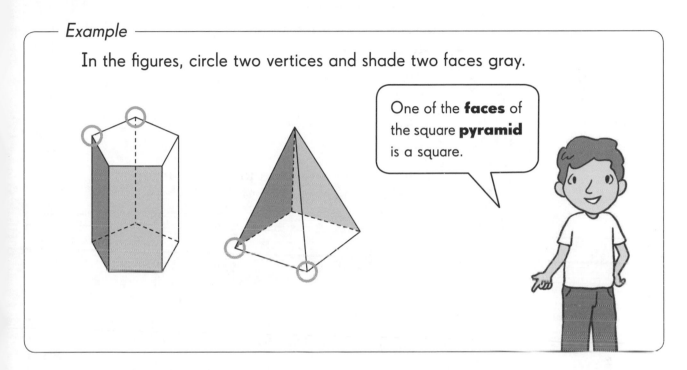

One of the **faces** of the square **pyramid** is a square.

1.   In the figures, circle three vertices and color three edges gray.

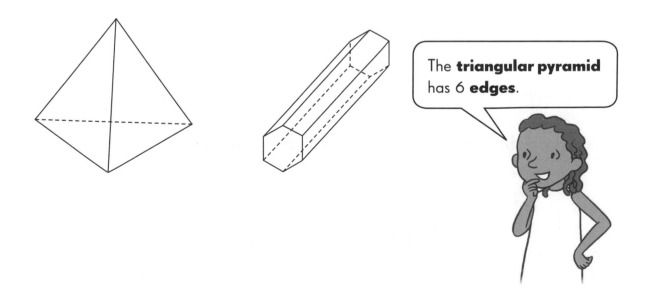

The **triangular pyramid** has 6 **edges**.

Circle the shape(s) that can be found in the figure.

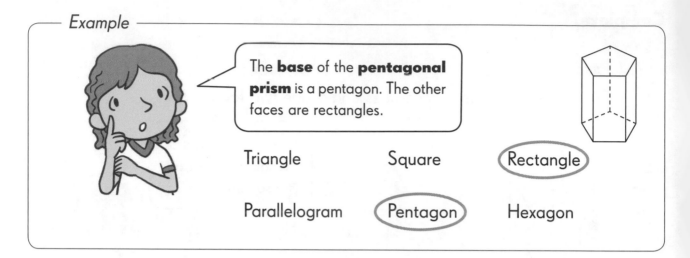

Example

The **base** of the **pentagonal prism** is a pentagon. The other faces are rectangles.

Triangle   Square   (Rectangle)

Parallelogram   (Pentagon)   Hexagon

2.   Triangle   Square   Rectangle

Parallelogram   Pentagon   Hexagon

Shade each solid shape if it has two identical and parallel faces.

3.

    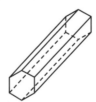

Put a check in the box if the solid figure is a prism.

4.

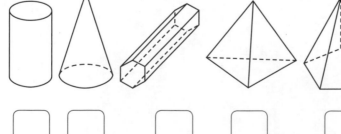
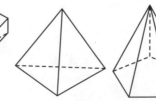
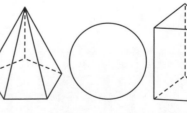

Match the names to the solid figures.

5.

Rectangular prism ●

Pentagonal prism ●

Triangular prism ●

Octagonal prism ●

Hexagonal prism ●

●

●

●

●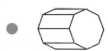

●

Complete the table.

	Type of Prism	Number of Faces	Number of Edges	Number of Vertices
6.	Rectangular			
7.	Pentagonal			
8.	Triangular			
9.	Octagonal			
10.	Hexagonal			

Put a check in the box if the solid figure is a pyramid.
Shade the base of each pyramid.

11.

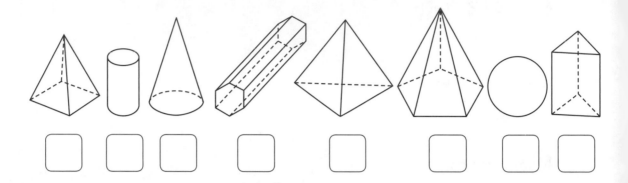

☐ ☐ ☐ ☐ ☐ ☐ ☐ ☐

Match the names to the solid figures.

12.

Triangular pyramid ●

Rectangular pyramid ●

Pentagonal pyramid ●

Hexagonal pyramid ●

Octagonal pyramid ●

●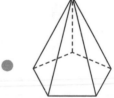

●

●

●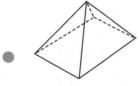

●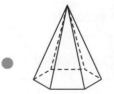

Name: _____ Date: _____

Complete the table.

	Type of Pyramid	Number of Faces	Number of Edges	Number of Vertices
13.	Triangular			
14.	Rectangular			
15.	Pentagonal			
16.	Hexagonal			
17.	Octagonal			

These are the nets of some pyramids.
Shade the base of each pyramid.

18.

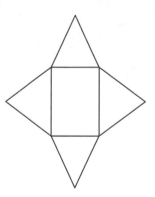

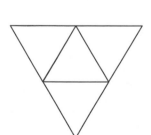

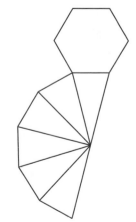

More than one **net** may form the same solid figure.

These are the nets of some prisms. Shade the identical and parallel edges of each prism using different colors.

19.

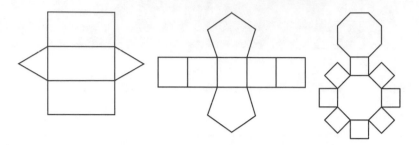

Match the nets with the solid figure they form.

20.

   •   •

   •   •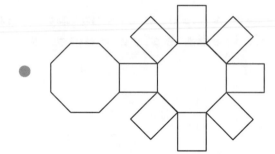

   •   •

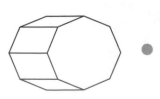   •   •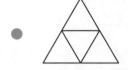

          •   •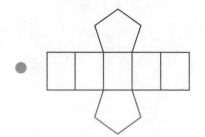

21.   Explain the statements.

a.   A cube is a rectangular prism.

b.   A cone is not a prism.

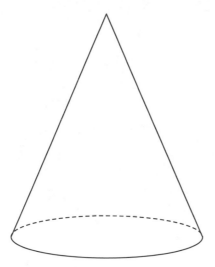

22. For each figure, identify whether or not it is a prism. Explain your reasoning.

Worksheet 4 Nets and Surface Area

Find the surface area of each cube.

Example

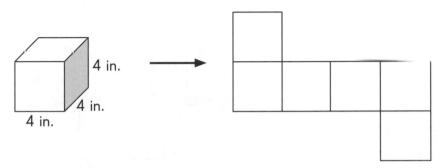

Area of one square face = 4 × 4
= 16 in.²

Surface area of the cube = 6 × 16
= 96 in.²

The **surface area** is equal to the sum of the areas of the 6 square faces.

1.

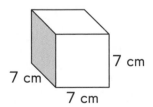

7 cm

7 cm

7 cm

2.

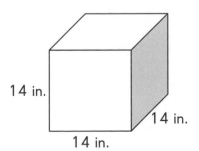

14 in.

14 in.

14 in.

Find the surface area of each rectangular prism.

Example

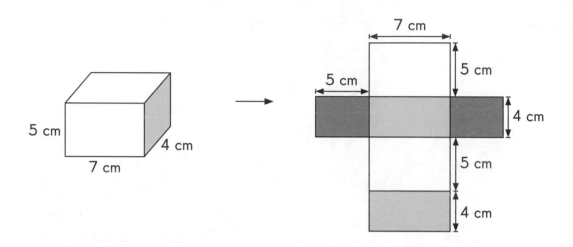

Area of 2 gray rectangles = ___(7 × 4)___ + ___(7 × 4)___

= _____2_____ × ___(7 × 4)___

= _____56 cm²_____

Area of 2 white rectangles = ___(7 × 5)___ + ___(7 × 5)___

= _____2_____ × ___(7 × 5)___

= _____70 cm²_____

Area of 2 black rectangles = ___(5 × 4)___ + ___(5 × 4)___

= _____2_____ × ___(5 × 4)___

= _____40 cm²_____

Surface area of the rectangular prism = 56 + 70 + 40

= 166 cm²

3.

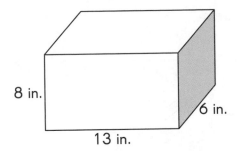

8 in.

13 in.

6 in.

4.

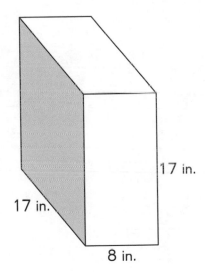

17 in.

17 in.

8 in.

5.

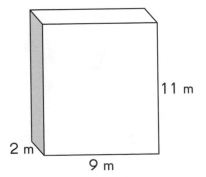

11 m

2 m

9 m

Find the surface area of each triangular prism.

Example

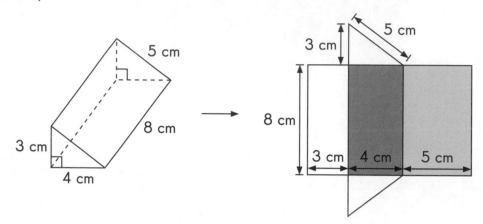

Area of triangles = ____2____ × ⟨ $\frac{(\frac{1}{2} \times 3 \times 4)}{}$ ⟩

= ____2____ × ____6____

= ___12 cm²___

Area of white rectangle = ____8____ × ____3____

= ___24 cm²___

Area of black rectangle = ___8 × 4___

= ___32 cm²___

Area of gray rectangle = ___8 × 5___

= ___40 cm²___

Surface area of the triangular prism = 12 + 24 + 32 + 40

= 108 cm²

6.

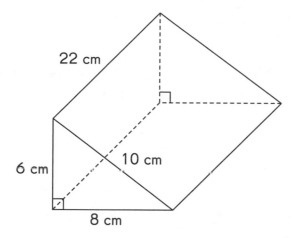

22 cm

6 cm

10 cm

8 cm

The base of this triangular prism is a **right triangle**.

7.

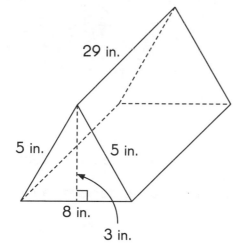

29 in.

5 in.

5 in.

8 in.

3 in.

Solve. Show your work.

8. A rectangular cupboard measures 110 centimeters by 85 centimeters by 40 centimeters. What is the surface area of the cupboard?

9. A rectangular display cabinet measures 96 centimeters by 78 centimeters by 34 centimeters. What is the surface area of the outside of the cabinet if it does not have a cover?

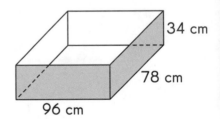

34 cm

78 cm

96 cm

10. A rectangular bedroom measures 12 feet by $8\frac{1}{2}$ feet by 7 feet. The rectangular door in the bedroom measures 2 feet by $6\frac{1}{2}$ feet. Joanne decides to paint the walls of the room pink. Find the surface area of the walls in the room.

Worksheet 5   Understanding and Measuring Volume

These solids are formed by stacking 1-centimeter cubes. Find the volume of each solid.

1.

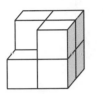

Volume = _____ cm^3

2.

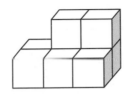

Volume = _____ cm^3

3.

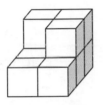

Volume = _____ cm^3

4.

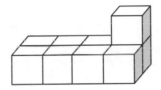

Volume = _____ cm^3

5.

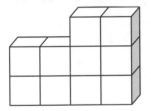

Volume = _____ cm^3

6.

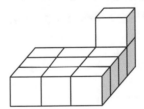

Volume = _____ cm^3

7.

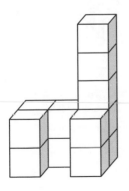

Volume = _____ cm^3

8.

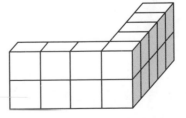

Volume = _____ cm^3

These solids are built using unit cubes. Find the volume of each solid. Then compare the volumes and fill in the blanks.

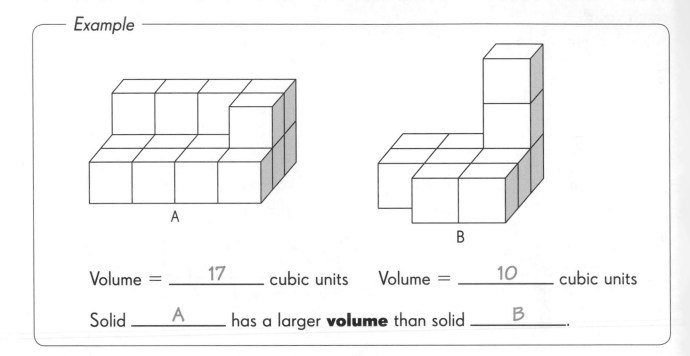

Example

Volume = _____17_____ cubic units   Volume = _____10_____ cubic units

Solid _____A_____ has a larger **volume** than solid _____B_____.

These solids are built using 1-inch cubes. Find the volume of each solid. Then compare their volumes and fill in the blanks.

9.

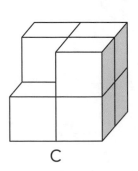

C

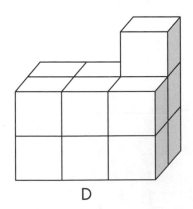

D

Volume = _____ in.³   Volume = _____ in.³

Solid _____ has a lesser volume than solid _____.

Name: _____   Date: _____

These solids are built using 1-foot cubes. Find the volume of each solid. Then compare their volumes and fill in the blanks.

10.

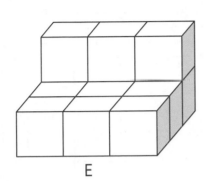

E

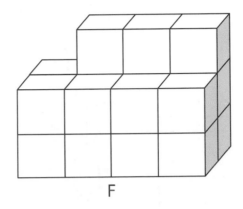

F

Volume = _____ ft³   Volume = _____ ft³

Solid _____ has a larger volume than solid _____.

These solids are built using 1-centimeter cubes. Find the volume of each solid. Then compare their volumes and fill in the blanks.

11.

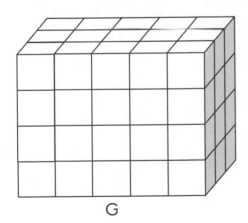

G

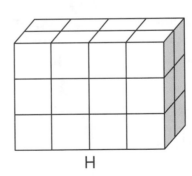

H

Length = _____ cm   Length = _____ cm

Width = _____ cm   Width = _____ cm

Height = _____ cm   Height = _____ cm

Volume = _____ cm³   Volume = _____ cm³

Solid _____ has a larger volume than solid _____.

These solids are built using 1-meter cubes. Find the volume of each solid. Then compare their volumes and fill in the blanks.

12.

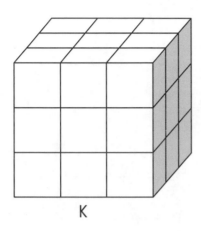

K

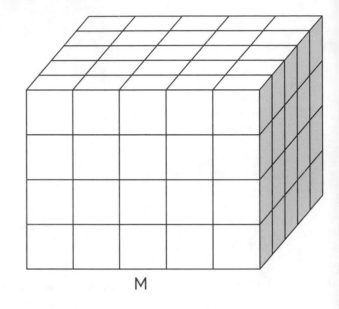

M

Length = _____ m   Length = _____ m

Width = _____ m   Width = _____ m

Height = _____ m   Height = _____ m

Volume = _____ m³   Volume = _____ m³

Solid _____ has a smaller volume than solid _____.

Worksheet 6   Volume of a Rectangular Prism and Liquid

Find the volume of each rectangular prism or cube.

Example

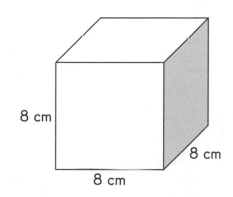

8 cm

8 cm

8 cm

Length = _____8_____ cm

Width = _____8_____ cm

Height = _____8_____ cm

Volume = length × width × height

= edge × edge × edge

= _____8_____ × _____8_____ × _____8_____

= _____512 cm³_____

1.

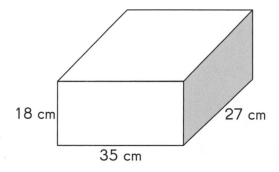

18 cm

27 cm

35 cm

Volume = _____

2.

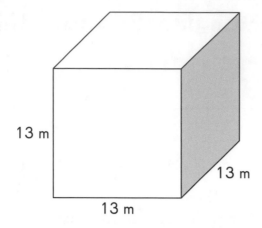

13 m

13 m

13 m

Volume = _____

3.

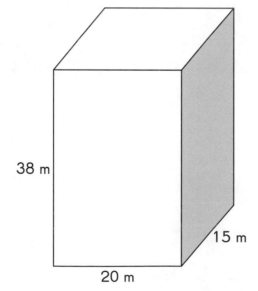

38 m

15 m

20 m

Volume = _____

4.

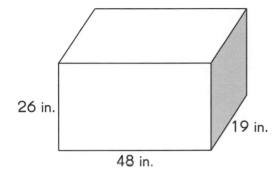

26 in.

19 in.

48 in.

Volume = _____

5.

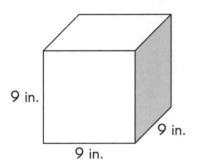

9 in.

9 in.

9 in.

Volume = _____

6.

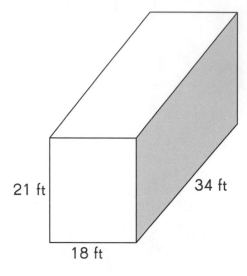

21 ft

34 ft

18 ft

Volume = _____

7.

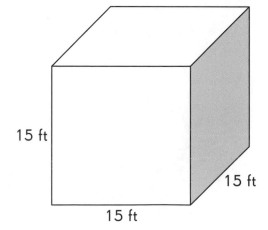

15 ft

15 ft

15 ft

Volume = _____

Solve. Show your work.

Example

Steven fills a rectangular container measuring 17 centimeters by 14.5 centimeters by 12 centimeters with orange juice. How many liters and milliliters of orange juice are in the container?

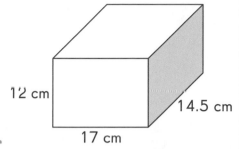

12 cm
14.5 cm
17 cm

Volume of orange juice in the container
= 17 cm × 14.5 cm × 12 cm
= 2,958 cm³
= 2,958 mL
= 2 L 958 mL

The **capacity** of a container is the liquid volume of the container.

Remember that 1 cm³ = 1 mL.

8. The base of a miniature rectangular fish tank measures 8 centimeters by 4.5 centimeters. The height of the tank is 6 centimeters. Find the capacity of the tank in liters and milliliters.

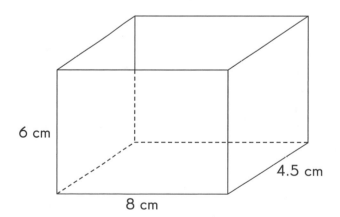

6 cm
4.5 cm
8 cm

9.   A rectangular container measures 6 centimeters by 3.5 centimeters by
12 centimeters. It is completely filled with water. How many liters and
milliliters of water are in the container?

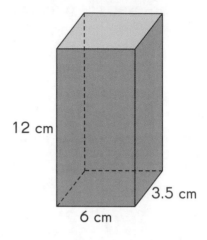

12 cm

3.5 cm

6 cm

10.   A rectangular box measures 15 centimeters by 9 centimeters by
13 centimeters. Shannon uses the box to mix glue for her project.
She fills the entire box with glue. How many liters and milliliters
of glue are in the box?

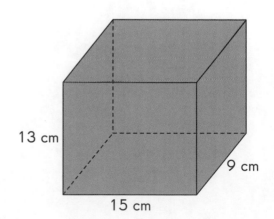

13 cm

9 cm

15 cm

11. A rectangular container is $\frac{1}{2}$-filled with water. How much water is needed to fill the container? After the container is filled, how much water must be poured out so that the container is $\frac{1}{3}$ full?

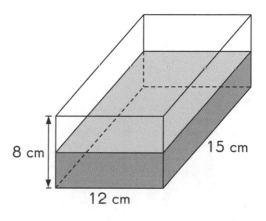

8 cm

15 cm

12 cm

12. A tank is $\frac{1}{2}$-filled with water. Some of the water is then poured into 8 small containers each with a capacity of 27 cubic centimeters. The tank is now $\frac{1}{4}$ full. What is the capacity of the tank?

13. A swimming pool, 25 meters wide, 50 meters long, and 12 meters deep, is $\frac{2}{3}$-filled with water. Its cross section is as shown below. How much water must be drained off so that the water level falls to 5 meters?

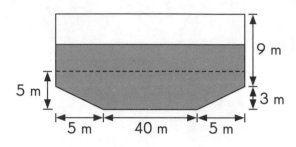

14. Complete the statements.

a. Volume of a rectangular prism = length × _____ × _____

b. Volume of a cube = _____ × width × _____

15. Label the two rectangular prisms.

Fill in the blanks with length, width and height.

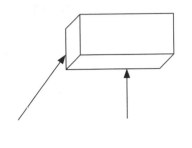

_____   _____

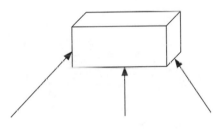

_____   _____   _____

16. In the diagram, the base = 63 m² and height = 8 m. Find the volume of the rectangular prism.

B = 63 m²

8 m

Volume = _____ cubic meters.

17. Find the volume of the prism.

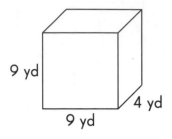

9 yd

9 yd

4 yd

Volume = _____

Worksheet 7   Volume of Composite Solids

Complete.

> *Example*
>
> A solid is made from two rectangular prisms. Find the volume of the solid.
>
>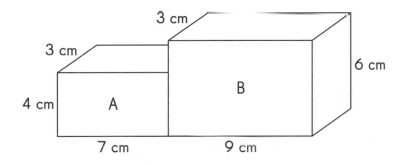
>
> **a.** Volume of prism A = __3__ × __4__ × __7__ = __84__ cm³
>
> **b.** Volume of prism B = __3__ × __6__ × __9__ = __162__ cm³
>
> **c.** Volume of the solid = __84__ + __162__ = __246__ cm³

1. A solid is made from two rectangular prisms.
Find the total volume of the solid.

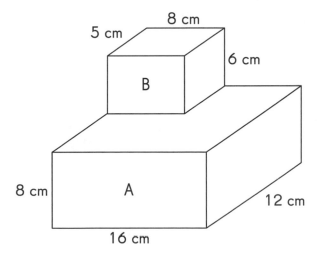

a. Volume of prism A = _____ × _____ × _____ = _____ cm³

b. Volume of prism B = _____ × _____ × _____ = _____ cm³

c. Volume of the solid = _____ + _____ = _____ cm³

Solve. Show your work.

2. Find the volume of the rectangular prism after a cube is removed from it.

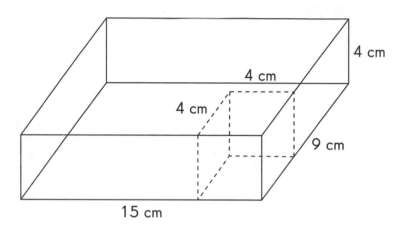

3. Find the volume of the solid which is made up of two prisms.

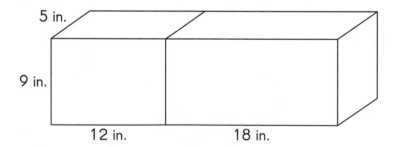

Answers

Chapter 8

Worksheet 1

1.
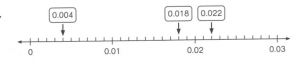

2. 0.017

3.
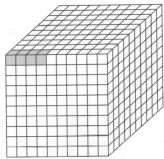

4.
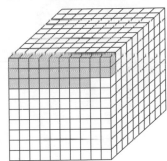

5.

Ones		Tenths	Hundredths	Thousandths
	○	○○	○○○○○	○○○○○○○

6. 1.423
7. 7
8. 540
9. 60
10. 37; 5
11. 0.107
12. 0.035
13. 0.393
14. 0.038
15. 0.007
16. 0.219
17. 0.035
18. 1.476
19. 2.005
20. 4.391
21. 3.056
22. 1.108

23. <u>2</u> ones and <u>8</u> tenths <u>1</u> hundredth <u>5</u> thousandths
24. <u>2</u> ones and <u>4</u> tenths <u>0</u> hundredths <u>9</u> thousandths
25. <u>7</u> ones and <u>0</u> tenths <u>9</u> hundredths <u>3</u> thousandths
26. <u>4</u> + <u>0.2</u> + <u>0.07</u> + <u>0.003</u>
27. <u>1</u> + <u>0.5</u> + <u>0.003</u>
28. <u>9</u> + <u>0.01</u> + <u>0.007</u>
29. 1; 6; 5
30. 5; 10; 100; 1000
31. 4; 7; 100; 8
32. 6; 9; 1000
33. 7; 5; 6; 1000
34. tenths
35. ones
36. thousandths
37. hundredths
38. 0.9
39. 0
40. 0.008
41. 6
42. 3 hundredths
43. tenths
44. thousandths
45. 7
46. 9.742
47. 5.814

Worksheet 2

1.

Ones		Tenths	Hundredths	Thousandths
0		1	0	8
0		1	2	0

Yes; Yes; No
<u>2</u> hundredths > <u>0</u> hundredths
0.12; 0.108

2. 3.9
3. 16.71
4. 105.67
5. 3.19
6. 99.89
7. 0.891
8. 133.2

9.

Ones		Tenths	Hundredths	Thousandths
4		8	5	7
4		8	5	2
4		8	5	4

Yes; Yes; Yes; No
<u>7</u> thousandths > <u>4</u> thousandths > <u>2</u> thousandths
4.852

10.

Ones	Tenths	Hundredths	Thousandths
5	2	7	3
5	2	9	1
5	2	4	8

Yes;   Yes;   No

<u>9</u> hundredths > <u>7</u> hundredths > <u>4</u> hundredths

5.291

11. (1.418) ~~1.814~~   12. (0.312) ~~0.37~~

13. (8.01) ~~8.181~~   14. (21.07) ~~27.1~~

15. (2.59) ~~2.95~~   16. (7.12) ~~7.22~~

17. (0.601) ~~0.641~~

18.

Ones	Tenths	Hundredths	Thousandths
3	5	8	6
0	3	1	4
3	5	6	7

No;   No;   No

<u>0.314</u>,   <u>3.567</u>,   <u>3.586</u>
least   greatest

19. 0.103,   0.131,   0.311

20. 0.15,   1.44,   5.14

21. 7.013,   7.033,   7.131

22. 9.009,   9.090,   9.900

23. 0.081,   0.118,   0.180

24. 3.639,   3.936,   3.963

25. 4.949,   9.449,   9.494

26. 0.62,   2.06,   6.02

27.

Ones	Tenths	Hundredths	Thousandths
2	3	9	6
1	4	3	1
2	3	0	2

No;   No;   No

<u>2.396</u>,   <u>2.302</u>,   <u>1.431</u>
greatest   least

28. 21.12,   12.21,   12.12

29. 0.110,   0.101,   0.011

30. 4.63,   4.36,   4.06

31. ⟨number line from 0.14 to 0.15 with X marked near right⟩
0.15

32. ⟨number line from 4.01 to 4.02 with X marked left⟩
4.01

	Decimal	Rounded to the Nearest		
		Whole Number	Tenth	Hundredth
33.	0.147	0	0.1	0.15
34.	2.564	3	2.6	2.56
35.	6.325	6	6.3	6.33

36. Answers vary.

Sample:

2.765, 2.766, 2.767, 2.768, or 2.769

37. 1.20

Worksheet 3

1. $\dfrac{4}{5}$

2. $5\dfrac{9}{10}$

3. $6\dfrac{1}{25}$

4. $\dfrac{47}{100}$

5. $\dfrac{9}{125}$

6. $7\dfrac{3}{200}$

7. $2\dfrac{109}{250}$

8. $2\dfrac{37}{1000}$

9. $4\dfrac{1}{125}$

10. $16\dfrac{3}{20}$

11. $\dfrac{377}{500}$

12. $\dfrac{1}{200}$

13. $4\dfrac{9}{25}$

14. $\dfrac{1}{50}$

15. $12\dfrac{3}{50}$

16. $11\dfrac{1}{125}$

17. $15\dfrac{13}{250}$

18. $17\dfrac{407}{500}$

19. $19\dfrac{3}{10}$

20. $9\dfrac{81}{200}$

21. $\dfrac{27}{250}$

22. $4\dfrac{7}{10}$

23. $\dfrac{3}{10}$

24. $1\dfrac{69}{200}$

25. $\dfrac{539}{1000}$

Chapter 9

Worksheet 1

1. 8; 8; 0.8
2. 9; 9; 0.9
3. 40; 40; 4.0
4. 16; 16; 1.6
5. 42; 42; 4.2
6. 0.6
7. 1.2
8. 2.4
9. 2.4
10. 4.0
11. 2.1
12. 4.5
13. $\underline{6}$ ones
14. $\underline{9}$ ones
15. $\underline{13}$ ones
16. $\underline{2}$ ones and $\underline{4}$ tenths
17. $\underline{3}$ ones and $\underline{7}$ tenths
18. $\underline{10}$ ones and $\underline{1}$ tenth
19. $\underline{24}$ tenths $-$ $\underline{2}$ ones and $\underline{4}$ tenths
20. $\underline{35}$ tenths $=$ $\underline{3}$ ones and $\underline{5}$ tenths
21. $\underline{48}$ tenths $=$ $\underline{4}$ ones and 8 tenths
22. $\underline{12}$ ones and $\underline{8}$ tenths
23. $\underline{42}$ ones and $\underline{6}$ tenths
24. $\underline{18}$ ones and $\underline{9}$ tenths
25. 7 tenths $\times$ 3 $=$ $\underline{21}$ tenths
    $\underline{21}$ tenths $=$ $\underline{2}$ ones and $\underline{1}$ tenth
    4 ones $\times$ 3 $=$ $\underline{12}$ ones
    $\underline{2}$ ones $+$ $\underline{12}$ ones $=$ $\underline{14}$ ones
    So, 4.7 $\times$ 3 $=$ $\underline{14.1}$.
26. 6 tenths $\times$ 4 $=$ $\underline{24}$ tenths
    $\underline{24}$ tenths $=$ $\underline{2}$ ones and $\underline{4}$ tenths
    5 ones $\times$ 4 $=$ $\underline{20}$ ones
    $\underline{2}$ ones $+$ $\underline{20}$ ones $=$ $\underline{22}$ ones
    So, 5.6 $\times$ 4 $=$ $\underline{22.4}$.
27. 8 tenths $\times$ 7 $=$ $\underline{56}$ tenths
    $\underline{56}$ tenths $=$ $\underline{5}$ ones and $\underline{6}$ tenths
    6 ones $\times$ 7 $=$ $\underline{42}$ ones
    $\underline{5}$ ones $+$ $\underline{42}$ ones $=$ $\underline{47}$ ones
    So, 6.8 $\times$ 7 $=$ $\underline{47.6}$.

28. 7 tenths $\times$ 4 $=$ $\underline{28}$ tenths
    $\underline{28}$ tenths $=$ $\underline{2}$ ones and $\underline{8}$ tenths
    3 ones $\times$ 4 $=$ $\underline{12}$ ones
    $\underline{2}$ ones $+$ $\underline{12}$ ones $=$ $\underline{14}$ ones
    So, 3.7 $\times$ 4 $=$ $\underline{14.8}$.
29. 6 tenths $\times$ 6 $=$ $\underline{36}$ tenths
    $\underline{36}$ tenths $=$ $\underline{3}$ ones and $\underline{6}$ tenths
    1 one $\times$ 6 $=$ $\underline{6}$ ones
    3 ones $+$ $\underline{6}$ ones $=$ $\underline{9}$ ones
    So, 1.6 $\times$ 6 $=$ $\underline{9.6}$.
30. 22.4
31. 32.9
32. 13.8
33. 9; 9; 0.09
34. 8; 8; 0.08
35. 0.06
36. 0.12
37. 0.16
38. 0.05
39. $\underline{4}$ tenths $\underline{7}$ hundredths
40. $\underline{8}$ tenths $\underline{0}$ hundredths
41. $\underline{5}$ tenths $\underline{9}$ hundredths
42. $\underline{12}$ hundredths $=$ $\underline{1}$ tenth $\underline{2}$ hundredths
43. $\underline{14}$ hundredths $=$ $\underline{1}$ tenth $\underline{4}$ hundredths
44. $\underline{28}$ hundredths $=$ $\underline{2}$ tenths $\underline{8}$ hundredths
45. $\underline{48}$ hundredths $=$ $\underline{4}$ tenths 8 hundredths
46. 0.12
47. 0.18
48. 0.15
49. 0.20
50. $\underline{6}$ tenths $+$ $\underline{2}$ tenths $\underline{4}$ hundredths
    $=$ $\underline{8}$ tenths $\underline{4}$ hundredths
51. $\underline{14}$ tenths $+$ $\underline{2}$ tenths $\underline{1}$ hundredth
    $=$ $\underline{16}$ tenths $\underline{1}$ hundredth
52. $\underline{24}$ tenths $+$ $\underline{1}$ tenth $\underline{6}$ hundredths
    $=$ $\underline{25}$ tenths $\underline{6}$ hundredths
53. 5 hundredths $\times$ 7 $=$ $\underline{35}$ hundredths
    $=$ $\underline{3}$ tenths $\underline{5}$ hundredths
    So, 0.05 $\times$ 7 $=$ $\underline{0.35}$.
54. 9 hundredths $\times$ 2 $=$ $\underline{18}$ hundredths
    $\underline{18}$ hundredths $=$ $\underline{1}$ tenth $\underline{8}$ hundredths
    4 tenths $\times$ 2 $=$ $\underline{8}$ tenths
    $\underline{1}$ tenth $+$ $\underline{8}$ tenths $=$ $\underline{9}$ tenths
    $\underline{9}$ tenths $=$ $\underline{0}$ ones and $\underline{9}$ tenths
    So, 0.49 $\times$ 2 $=$ $\underline{0.98}$.

55. 5 hundredths $\times$ 3 = $\underline{15}$ hundredths
$\underline{15}$ hundredths = $\underline{1}$ tenth $\underline{5}$ hundredths
2 tenths $\times$ 3 = $\underline{6}$ tenths
$\underline{1}$ tenth + $\underline{6}$ tenths = $\underline{7}$ tenths
$\underline{7}$ tenths = $\underline{0}$ ones and $\underline{7}$ tenths
So, 0.25 $\times$ 3 = $\underline{0.75}$.

56. 3 hundredths $\times$ 4 = $\underline{12}$ hundredths
$\underline{12}$ hundredths = $\underline{1}$ tenth $\underline{2}$ hundredths
4 tenths $\times$ 4 = $\underline{16}$ tenths
$\underline{1}$ tenth + $\underline{16}$ tenths = $\underline{17}$ tenths
$\underline{17}$ tenths = $\underline{1}$ one and $\underline{7}$ tenths
So, 0.43 $\times$ 4 = $\underline{1.72}$.

57. 7 hundredths $\times$ 5 = $\underline{35}$ hundredths
$\underline{35}$ hundredths = $\underline{3}$ tenths $\underline{5}$ hundredths
6 tenths $\times$ 5 = $\underline{30}$ tenths
$\underline{3}$ tenths + $\underline{30}$ tenths = $\underline{33}$ tenths
$\underline{33}$ tenths = $\underline{3}$ ones and $\underline{3}$ tenths
So, 0.67 $\times$ 5 = $\underline{3.35}$.

58. 4.35

59. 9.44

60. 21.48

Worksheet 2

1. 12.8		2. 47.5
3. 3.6		4. 9.2
5. 34.5		6. 8.1
7. 64		8. 78
9. 7		10. 9
11. 53		12. 4
13. 3.75		14. 2.84
15. 16.93		16. 24.38
17. 7.36		18. 89.31
19. 13.9		20. 24.7
21. 8.4		22. 9.4
23. 72		24. 63
25. 8		26. 2
27. 4.81		28. 1.79
29. 24.35		30. 65.82
31. 10		32. 10
33. 10		34. 10
35. 1.208		36. 0.103
37. 0.305		38. 24.58

39. 4	40. 10
41. 15	42. 10
43. 10	44. 9
45. 10	46. 17

47. 6 $\times$ $\underline{7}$ $\times$ 10 = $\underline{42}$ $\times$ 10 = $\underline{420}$
48. $\underline{8}$ $\times$ $\underline{12}$ $\times$ 10 = $\underline{96}$ $\times$ 10 = $\underline{960}$
49. $\underline{11}$ $\times$ $\underline{5}$ $\times$ 10 = $\underline{55}$ $\times$ 10 = $\underline{550}$
50. $\underline{16}$ $\times$ $\underline{18}$ $\times$ 10 = $\underline{288}$ $\times$ 10 = $\underline{2,880}$

51. 63	52. 45
53. 4.8	54. 7.8
55. 7.5	56. 5.4
57. 725.8	58. 659
59. 141.3	60. 15.36
61. 137.5	62. 267.9
63. 47.2	64. 81.4
65. 578	66. 693
67. 38	68. 91
69. 6,379.2	70. 4,183.5
71. 38.4	72. 17.2
73. 1,492	74. 2,679
75. 385	76. 496
77. 4,670	78. 5,820
79. 400	80. 100
81. 100	82. 1,000
83. 100	84. 1,000
85. 0.369	86. 0.204
87. 0.048	88. 0.91
89. 5	90. 1,000
91. 9	92. 100
93. 100	94. 6
95. 1,000	96. 26

97. 3 $\times$ $\underline{8}$ $\times$ 1,000 = $\underline{24}$ $\times$ 1,000 = $\underline{24,000}$
98. $\underline{7}$ $\times$ $\underline{11}$ $\times$ 100 = $\underline{77}$ $\times$ 100 = $\underline{7,700}$
99. $\underline{12}$ $\times$ $\underline{6}$ $\times$ 1,000 = $\underline{72}$ $\times$ 1,000 = $\underline{72,000}$

100. 32,000	101. 5,400
102. 30,000	103. 5,600
104. 91	105. 9,600
106. 900	107. 680

108. $10^2 = \underline{10} \times \underline{10}$

109. $10^3 = \underline{10} \times \underline{10} \times \underline{10}$

110. 1,000

111. 100

112. 725.8

113. 329.5

114. 47.1

115. 3.84

116. 3,792

117. 1,835

118. 38.4

119. 17.2

120. 247.8

121. 58.7

122. 1,369.5

123. 47.8

Worksheet 3

1. 3

2. 3

3. 5

4. 4

5. 4

6. 8

7. 8

8. 23

9. 5

10. 4

11. 7

12. 14

13. 9

14.

```
    ┌─┐
    │2│
    └─┘
 2)4 . 6
   ┌─┐
   │4│
   └─┘
   ┌─┐
   │0│
   └─┘
```

Divide the ones by 2.
4 ones ÷ 2 = 2 ones

```
   ┌─┐ ┌─┐
   │2│.│3│
   └─┘ └─┘
 2)4 . 6
   ┌─┐
   │4│
   └─┘
   ┌─┐ ┌─┐
   │0│ │6│
   └─┘ └─┘
       ┌─┐
       │6│
       └─┘
       ┌─┐
       │0│
       └─┘
```

Divide the tenths by 2.
6 tenths ÷ 2 = 3 tenths
So, 4.6 ÷ 2 = 2.3.

15.

```
    ┌─┐
    │2│
    └─┘
 3)6 . 9
   ┌─┐
   │6│
   └─┘
   ┌─┐
   │0│
   └─┘
```

Divide the ones by 3.
6 ones ÷ 3 = 2 ones

```
   ┌─┐ ┌─┐
   │2│.│3│
   └─┘ └─┘
 3)6 . 9
   ┌─┐
   │6│
   └─┘
   ┌─┐ ┌─┐
   │0│ │9│
   └─┘ └─┘
       ┌─┐
       │9│
       └─┘
       ┌─┐
       │0│
       └─┘
```

Divide the tenths by 3.
9 tenths ÷ 3 = 3 tenths
So, 6.9 ÷ 3 = 2.3.

16.

```
    ┌─┐
    │2│
    └─┘
 4)8 . 4
   ┌─┐
   │8│
   └─┘
   ┌─┐
   │0│
   └─┘
```

Divide the ones by 4.
8 ones ÷ 4 = 2 ones

```
   ┌─┐ ┌─┐
   │2│.│1│
   └─┘ └─┘
 4)8 . 4
   ┌─┐
   │8│
   └─┘
   ┌─┐ ┌─┐
   │0│ │4│
   └─┘ └─┘
       ┌─┐
       │4│
       └─┘
       ┌─┐
       │0│
       └─┘
```

Divide the tenths by 4.
4 tenths ÷ 4 = 1 tenth
So, 8.4 ÷ 4 = 2.1.

17.

```
   ┌─┐ ┌─┐
   │1│.│3│
   └─┘ └─┘
 3)3 . 9
   ┌─┐
   │3│
   └─┘
   ┌─┐ ┌─┐
   │0│ │9│
   └─┘ └─┘
       ┌─┐
       │9│
       └─┘
       ┌─┐
       │0│
       └─┘
```

18.

$$0.8$$

$$3\overline{)2\ .\ 4}$$
$$0$$
$$2\quad4$$
$$2\quad4$$
$$0$$

19.

$$0\ .\ 9$$

$$6\overline{)5\ .\ 4}$$
$$0$$
$$5\quad4$$
$$5\quad4$$
$$0$$

20.

$$0\ .\ 1$$

$$7\overline{)0\ .\ 7}$$
$$0$$
$$0\quad7$$
$$7$$
$$0$$

21.

$$0\ .\ 4$$

$$8\overline{)3\ .\ 2}$$
$$0$$
$$3\quad2$$
$$3\quad2$$
$$0$$

22. 3 ones = 2 ones and 10 tenths
3 ones and 6 tenths
= 2 ones and 10 tenths + 6 tenths
= 2 ones and 16 tenths
2 ones and 16 tenths 8 hundredths ÷ 2
= 1 one and 8 tenths 4 hundredths

23. 5 tenths = 3 tenths 20 hundredths
5 tenths 4 hundredths
= 3 tenths 20 hundredths + 4 hundredths
= 3 tenths 24 hundredths
6 ones and 3 tenths 24 hundredths ÷ 3
= 2 ones and 1 tenth 8 hundredths

24. 6 tenths = 4 tenths 20 hundredths
6 tenths 4 hundredths
= 4 tenths 20 hundredths + 4 hundredths
= 4 tenths 24 hundredths
4 ones and 4 tenths 24 hundredths ÷ 4
= 1 one and 1 tenth 6 hundredths

25. 4 ones = 3 ones and 10 tenths
9 tenths 5 hundredths
= 8 tenths 10 hundredths + 5 hundredths
= 8 tenths 15 hundredths
3 ones and 18 tenths 15 hundredths ÷ 3
= 1 one and 6 tenths 5 hundredths

26. 6 ones = 5 ones and 10 tenths
6 ones and 5 tenths
= 5 ones and 10 tenths + 5 tenths
= 5 ones and 15 tenths
5 ones and 15 tenths 5 hundredths ÷ 5
= 1 one and 3 tenths 1 hundredth

27.

$$2$$
$$3\overline{)6\ .\ 5\quad7}$$
$$6$$
$$0$$

Divide the ones by 3.
6 ones ÷ 3 = 2 ones

$$2\ .\ 1$$
$$3\overline{)6\ .\ 5\quad7}$$
$$6$$
$$0\quad5$$
$$3$$
$$2$$

Divide the tenths by 3.
5 tenths ÷ 3
= 1 tenth R 2 tenths
2 tenths = 20 hundredths

$$2\ .\ 1$$
$$3\overline{)6\ .\ 5\quad7}$$
$$6$$
$$0\quad5$$
$$3$$
$$2\quad7$$

Add the hundredths.
20 hundredths +
7 hundredths
= 27 hundredths

$$2\ .\ 1\quad9$$
$$3\overline{)6\ .\ 5\quad7}$$
$$6$$
$$0\quad5$$
$$3$$
$$2\quad7$$
$$2\quad7$$
$$0$$

Divide the hundredths by 3.
27 hundredths ÷ 3
= 9 hundredths
So, 6.57 ÷ 3 = 2.19.

28.

```
      2 . 1 8
  4) 8 . 7 2
     8
     0 7
       4
       3 2
       3 2
         0
```

29.

```
      1 . 0 7
  6) 6 . 4 2
     6
     0 4
       0
       4 2
       4 2
         0
```

30.

```
      2
  2) 5 . 4 8
     4
     1
```

Divide the ones by 2.
5 ones ÷ 2
= 2 ones R 1 one

```
      2
  2) 5 . 4 8
     4
     1 4
```

Regroup the remainder 1 one.
1 one = 10 tenths
Add the tenths.
10 tenths + 4 tenths
= 14 tenths

```
      2 . 7
  2) 5 . 4 8
     4
     1 4
     1 4
       0
```

Divide the tenths by 2.
14 tenths ÷ 2 = 7 tenths

```
      2 . 7 4
  2) 5 . 4 8
     4
     1 4
     1 4
       0 8
         8
         0
```

Divide the hundredths by 2.
8 hundredths ÷ 2
= 4 hundredths
So, 5.48 ÷ 2 = 2.74.

31.

```
      2
  3) 6 . 7 8
     6
     0
```

Divide the ones by 3.
6 ones ÷ 3
= 2 ones

```
      2 . 2
  3) 6 . 7 8
     6
     0 7
       6
       1
```

Divide the tenths by 3.
7 tenths ÷ 3
= 2 tenths R 1 tenth

```
      2 . 2
  3) 6 . 7 8
     6
     0 7
       6
       1 8
```

Regroup the remainder 1 tenth.
1 tenth = 10 hundredths
Add the hundredths.
10 hundredths +
8 hundredths
= 18 hundredths

```
      2 . 2 6
  3) 6 . 7 8
     6
     0 7
       6
       1 8
       1 8
         0
```

Divide the hundredths by 3.
18 hundredths ÷ 3
= 6 hundredths
So, 6.78 ÷ 3 = 2.26.

32.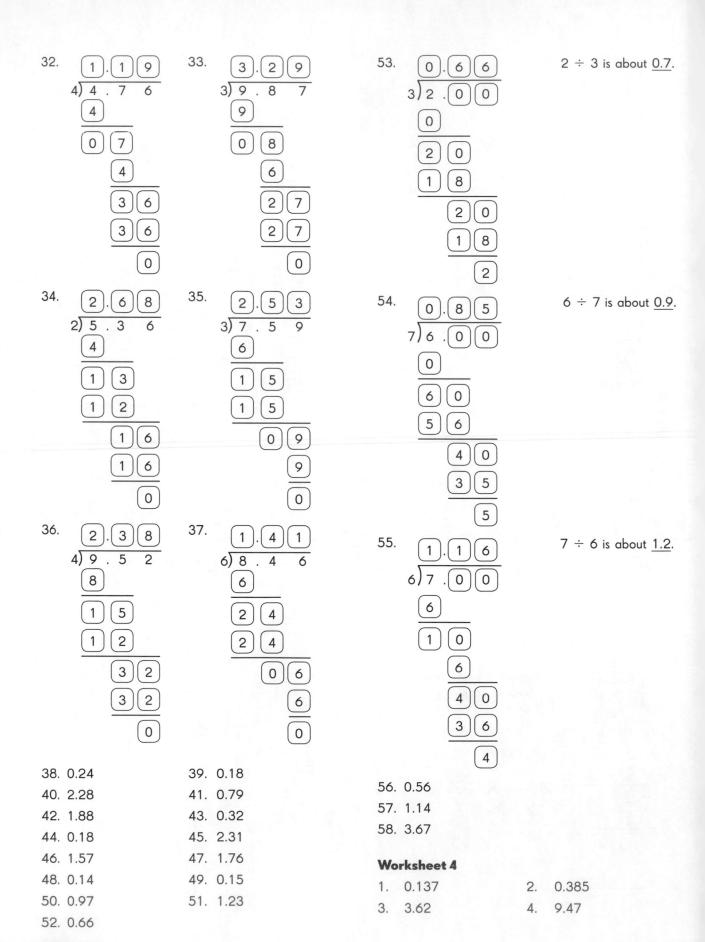

33.

53.

2 ÷ 3 is about 0.7.

34.

35.

54.

6 ÷ 7 is about 0.9.

36.

37.

55.

7 ÷ 6 is about 1.2.

38. 0.24
40. 2.28
42. 1.88
44. 0.18
46. 1.57
48. 0.14
50. 0.97
52. 0.66

39. 0.18
41. 0.79
43. 0.32
45. 2.31
47. 1.76
49. 0.15
51. 1.23

56. 0.56
57. 1.14
58. 3.67

Worksheet 4
1. 0.137
3. 3.62

2. 0.385
4. 9.47

5. 64.5
6. 78.6
7. 0.09
8. 0.04
9. 0.284
10. 46.3
11. 0.095
12. 7.26
13. 10
14. 10
15. 10
16. 10
17. 30.9
18. 704
19. 0.5
20. 4.58
21. 3
22. 2
23. 280
24. 420
25. $(60 \div \underline{2}) \div 10 = \underline{30} \div 10 = \underline{3}$
26. $(120 \div \underline{3}) \div 10 = \underline{40} \div 10 = \underline{4}$
27. $(\underline{360} \div 4) \div 10 = \underline{90} \div 10 = \underline{9}$
28. $(\underline{560} \div 8) \div 10 = \underline{70} \div 10 = \underline{7}$
29. $(\underline{16} \div 8) \div 10 = \underline{2} \div 10 = \underline{0.2}$
30. $(\underline{21} \div 7) : 10 = \underline{3} \div 10 = \underline{0.3}$
31. $(\underline{0.9} \div 3) \div 10 = \underline{0.3} \div 10 = \underline{0.03}$
32. $(\underline{0.15} \div 5) \div 10 = \underline{0.03} \div 10 = \underline{0.003}$
33. 0.02
34. 0.2
35. 0.3
36. 0.015
37. 0.006
38. 0.238
39. 0.473
40. 0.375
41. 0.984
42. 0.059
43. 0.027
44. 0.147
45. 0.258
46. 0.069
47. 0.038
48. 1.234
49. 6.101
50. 100
51. 1,000
52. 1,000
53. 100
54. 408
55. 205
56. 7
57. 852
58. 2
59. 3
60. 40
61. 6
62. 0.9
63. 2
64. 3
65. 180
66. 8
67. 0.8
68. 0.2
69. 0.02
70. 0.4
71. 0.09
72. 0.004
73. 0.005
74. 0.05
75. 0.02
76. 0.002
77. 0.015
78. 0.003
79. 0.008
80. 0.07
81. 0.15
82. 2.8
83. 5

Worksheet 5

1. 4 tenths is <u>less than</u> <u>5</u> tenths.
   12.459 → <u>12</u>
   12

2. 6 tenths is <u>greater than</u> <u>5</u> tenths.
   43.607 → <u>44</u>
   44

3. 9 tenths is <u>greater than</u> <u>5</u> tenths.
   28.910 → <u>29</u>
   29

4. 4 hundredths is <u>less than</u> <u>5</u> hundredths.
   6.341 → <u>6.3</u>
   6.3

5. 5 hundredths is <u>equal to</u> <u>5</u> hundredths.
   17.251 → <u>17.3</u>
   17.3

6. 0 hundredths is <u>less than</u> 5 hundredths.
   39.908 → <u>39.9</u>
   39.9

7. 7 hundredths is <u>greater than</u> <u>5</u> hundredths.
   18.472 → <u>18.5</u>
   18.5

8. 6 thousandths is <u>greater than</u> <u>5</u> thousandths.
   16.016 → <u>16.02</u>
   16.02

9. 5 thousandths is <u>equal to</u> <u>5</u> thousandths.
   24.005 → <u>24.01</u>
   24.01

10. 6 thousandths is <u>greater than</u> <u>5</u> thousandths.
    45.076 → <u>45.08</u>
    45.08

11. 1.62 → <u>2</u> ; 3.39 → <u>3</u>
    <u>2</u> + <u>3</u> = <u>5</u>
    5

12. 4.53 → <u>5</u> ; 0.82 → <u>1</u>
    <u>5</u> + <u>1</u> = <u>6</u>
    6

13. 7.49 → <u>7</u> ; 2.39 → <u>2</u>
    <u>7</u> + <u>2</u> = <u>9</u>
    9

14. $18.57 \longrightarrow \underline{19}$; $9.98 \longrightarrow \underline{10}$
$\underline{19} + \underline{10} = \underline{29}$
29

15. $4.67 \longrightarrow \underline{5}$; $0.88 \longrightarrow \underline{1}$
$\underline{5} + \underline{1} = \underline{6}$
6

16. $7.39 \longrightarrow \underline{7.4}$; $2.91 \longrightarrow \underline{2.9}$
$\underline{7.4} - \underline{2.9} = \underline{4.5}$
4.5

17. 2.4   18. 7.7

19. 8.9   20. 22.7

21. $3.51 \longrightarrow \underline{4}$
$\underline{4} \times \underline{7} = \underline{28}$
28

22. 96   23. 176

24. 216   25. 351

26. $4.54 \longrightarrow \underline{4.5}$
$\underline{4.5} \times \underline{6} = \underline{27}$
27

27. 100.1   28. 152.1

29. $31.52 \longrightarrow \underline{32}$
$\underline{32} \div \underline{8} = \underline{4}$
4

30. 8   31. 9

32. $37.24 \longrightarrow \underline{37.2}$
$\underline{37.2} \div \underline{6} = \underline{6.2}$

33. 2.7   34. 7.3

Worksheet 6

1. 8   2. 9

3. 1.5   4. 4.7

5. 790   6. 1,234

7. $0.4 \times \underline{100}$
$= \underline{40}$ cm

8. $7.43 \times \underline{100}$
$= \underline{743}$ cm

9. $\underline{1.585} \times \underline{100}$
$= \underline{158.5}$ cm

10. $\underline{500.75} \times \underline{100}$
$= \underline{50,075}$ cm

11. $0.09 \times \underline{100}$
$= \underline{9}$ cm
15.09 m $= \underline{15}$ m $\underline{9}$ cm

12. $0.8 \times \underline{100}$
$= \underline{80}$ cm
224.8 m $= \underline{224}$ m $\underline{80}$ cm

13. $\underline{35}$ m $\underline{9}$ cm   14. $\underline{158}$ m $\underline{60}$ cm

15. 40   16. 70

17. 26   18. 38

19. 6,200   20. 45,670

21. $0.6 \times \underline{1,000} = \underline{600}$ m

22. $8.32 \times \underline{1,000} = \underline{8,320}$ m

23. $\underline{1.493} \times \underline{1,000} = \underline{1,493}$ m

24. $\underline{300.92} \times \underline{1,000} = \underline{300,920}$ m

25. $7.04 \times \underline{1,000} = \underline{7,040}$ g

26. $25.8 \times \underline{1,000} = \underline{25,800}$ g

27. $9.05 \times \underline{1,000} = \underline{9,050}$ g

28. $14.2 \times \underline{1,000} = \underline{14,200}$ g

29. $5.08 \times \underline{1,000} = \underline{5,080}$ mL

30. $14.3 \times \underline{1,000} = \underline{14,300}$ mL

31. $\underline{3.07} \times \underline{1,000} = \underline{3,070}$ mL

32. $\underline{26.4} \times \underline{1,000} = \underline{26,400}$ mL

33. $0.07 \times \underline{1,000} = \underline{70}$ m
46.07 km $= \underline{46}$ km $\underline{70}$ m

34. $\underline{0.9} \times \underline{1,000}$
$= \underline{900}$ m
168.9 km $= \underline{168}$ km $\underline{900}$ m

35. $\underline{57}$ km $\underline{40}$ m

36. $\underline{248}$ km $\underline{500}$ m

37. $\underline{0.05} \times \underline{1,000}$
$= \underline{50}$ g
2.05 kg $= \underline{2}$ kg $\underline{50}$ g

38. $\underline{0.9} \times \underline{1,000}$
$= \underline{900}$ g
12.9 kg $= \underline{12}$ kg $\underline{900}$ g

39. $\underline{9}$ kg $\underline{30}$ g

40. $\underline{21}$ kg $\underline{600}$ g

41. $\underline{0.03} \times \underline{1,000}$
$= \underline{30}$ mL
8.03 L $= \underline{8}$ L $\underline{30}$ mL

42. $\underline{0.7} \times \underline{1,000}$
$= \underline{700}$ mL
24.7 L $= \underline{24}$ L $\underline{700}$ mL

43. $\underline{7}$ L $\underline{10}$ mL

44. $\underline{15}$ L $\underline{800}$ mL

45. $25.4 \div \underline{100}$
$= \underline{0.254}$ m

46. $9.83 \div \underline{100}$
$= \underline{0.0983}$ m

47. $32.5 \div \underline{100}$
    $= \underline{0.325}$ m

48. $127.6 \div \underline{100}$
    $= \underline{1.276}$ m

49. $\underline{40} \div 100$
    $= \underline{0.4}$ m
    29 m 40 cm $= \underline{29.4}$ m

50. $\underline{80} \div 100$
    $= \underline{0.8}$ m
    15 m 80 cm $= \underline{15.8}$ m

51. 26.9

52. 145.3

53. $4,970 \div \underline{1,000}$
    $= \underline{4.97}$ km

54. 2.587

55. 12.783

56. $826 \div \underline{1,000}$
    $= \underline{0.826}$ kg

57. 4.458

58. 0.997

59. $773 \div \underline{1,000}$
    $= \underline{0.773}$ L

60. 0.335

61. 4.785

62. $8 \div \underline{1,000}$
    $= \underline{0.008}$ km
    5 km $+ \underline{0.008}$ km
    $= \underline{5.008}$ km

63. 32.074

64. 66.009

65. $600 \div \underline{1,000}$
    $= \underline{0.6}$ kg
    $\underline{75}$ kg $+ \underline{0.6}$ kg
    $= \underline{75.6}$ kg

66. 66.09

67. 175.175

68. $900 \div \underline{1,000}$
    $= \underline{0.9}$ L
    $\underline{124}$ L $+ \underline{0.9}$ L
    $= \underline{124.9}$ L

69. 78.045

70. 255.75

71. a. The distance is 8,250 meters.

    b. 8.25 km

72. The truck can carry a maximum of 84 bags of rice.

73. The total volume that the containers carry is 144 liters.

74. He needs to buy 55 meters of cloth.

Worksheet 7

1. 3.2 cm → $\underline{3}$ cm
   $\underline{3} \times \underline{4} = \underline{12}$ cm
   The total length is about $\underline{12}$ centimeters.

2. 7.57 cm → 8 cm
   $8 \times 6 = 48$ cm
   The total length is about $\underline{48}$ centimeters.

3. 78.65 →
   $6 \times \underline{12} = \underline{72}$
   $6 \times \underline{13} = \underline{78}$
   $6 \times \underline{14} = \underline{84}$
   $\underline{78.65}$ is nearer to 78.
   Since $6 \times \underline{13} = 78$, each child gets about $\underline{\$13}$.

4. 65 →
   $4 \times \underline{15} = \underline{60}$
   $4 \times \underline{16} = \underline{64}$
   $4 \times \underline{17} = \underline{68}$
   $\underline{64}$ is nearer to 65.
   Since $4 \times \underline{16} = \underline{64}$, the length of each cut part of the rope is about $\underline{16}$ meters.

5. $2.65 → $3
   $1.89 → $2
   $4.57 → $5
   $1.66 → $2
   $2.65 + $1.89 + $4.57 + $1.66
   $\approx$ $3 + $2 + $5 + $2 = $12
   Yes, Jennifer has enough money to buy all four items.

6. 2.17 liters $\times 9 = 19.53$ liters
   $\approx$ 20 liters
   The capacity of the larger bucket is about 20 liters.

7. 15.67 mi $-$ 8.92 mi $= 6.75$ mi
   $\approx$ 7 mi
   The distance between the café and the school is about 7 miles.

8. 9.33 min $-$ 7.5 min $= 1.83$ min
   $\approx$ 2 min
   He must shave about 2 minutes off his best time to achieve his goal.

Chapter 10

Worksheet 1

1. 34
2. 34
3. 66
4. 66
5. 18
6. 55
7. 63
8. 90; 90
9. 70; 70
10. 80; 80
11. 40; 40
12. 79; 79
13. 46; 46
14. 1; 1
15. 8; 8
16. 9; 9
17. $\frac{21}{100}$
18. $\frac{63}{100}$
19. $\frac{9}{100}$
20. $\frac{3}{100}$
21. 37; 0.37
22. 94; 0.94
23. 5; 0.05
24. 9; 0.09
25. $\frac{9}{25}$
26. $\frac{3}{20}$
27. $\frac{18}{25}$
28. $\frac{9}{50}$
29. 42; $\frac{21}{50}$
30. 75; $\frac{3}{4}$
31. 8; $\frac{2}{25}$
32. 5; $\frac{1}{20}$

	Percent	Decimal
33. 7 out of 100	7	0.07
34. 4 out of 10	40	0.4
35. 9 out of 10	90	0.9

	Decimal	Fraction
36. 0%	0	0
37. 8%	0.08	$\frac{2}{25}$
38. 33%	0.33	$\frac{33}{100}$
39. 74%	0.74	$\frac{37}{50}$
40. 100%	1.0	$\frac{100}{100}$

		Percent	Fraction
41.	0	0	0
42.	0.7	70	$\frac{7}{10}$
43.	0.44	44	$\frac{11}{25}$
44.	0.73	73	$\frac{73}{100}$
45.	1	100	1

46. 45; 55
47. 30; 70
48. 35; 65
49. 76; 24

50.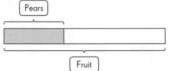

51. Adults / Visitors

Worksheet 2

1. 55; 55
2. 94; 94
3. 60; 60
4. 75; 75
5. 68; 68
6. $\frac{31}{50}$; 1; $\frac{31}{50}$; 100; 62
7. $\frac{9}{20}$; 1; $\frac{9}{20}$; 100; 45
8. 22; 22
9. 17; 17
10. 25; 25
11. 53; 53
12. 5; 65; 65
13. 4; 36; 36

14. 1 unit ⟶ 4%
    7 units ⟶ 28%

    Homework completed = 28%
    Homework not completed = 72%

15. 5 units ⟶ 100%
    1 unit ⟶ 20%
    4 units ⟶ 80%

    a. Kenneth did 80% of his homework.

    b. 20% of his homework was left undone.

16. $\frac{18}{25} \times 100\% = 72\%$

    $100\% - 72\% = 28\%$

    28% of Ahmad's land was planted with orange trees.

17. $\frac{1}{4} + \frac{1}{5} = \frac{9}{20}$

Fraction of journey completed $= \frac{9}{20}$

$\underline{20}$ units $\longrightarrow 100\%$
1 unit $\longrightarrow \underline{5}\%$
$\underline{11}$ units $\longrightarrow \underline{55}\%$

Fraction of the trail not completed

$= 1 - \frac{9}{20}$

$= \frac{11}{20}$

Percent of the trail not completed $= \underline{55}\%$

18. $\frac{1}{3} + \frac{5}{12} = \frac{3}{4}$

Fraction of fruit that was apples and

oranges $= \frac{3}{4}$

4 units $\longrightarrow 100\%$
1 unit $\longrightarrow 25\%$

Percent of fruit that was pears $= 25\%$

19. $\frac{1}{2} + \frac{1}{4} = \frac{3}{4}$

Fraction of pizza given away $= \frac{3}{4}$

4 units $\longrightarrow 100\%$
1 unit $\longrightarrow 25\%$

Percent of pizza left $= 25\%$

Worksheet 3

1. 0.3; 15
2. 0.4; 24
3. $\frac{70}{100}$; 150; 105
4. $\frac{45}{100}$; 320; 144

5. **Method 1:**

40% of 480 eggs $= \frac{40}{100} \times \underline{480}$

$= \underline{192}$

$\underline{192}$ eggs hatched.

Method 2:

100% $\longrightarrow \underline{480}$ eggs
1% $\longrightarrow \underline{4.8}$ eggs
40% $\longrightarrow \underline{192}$ eggs

$\underline{192}$ eggs hatched.

6. **Method 1:**

60% of $850 $= \frac{60}{100} \times \$850$

$= \$510$

Mrs. Smith spent $510 on the gifts.

Method 2:

100% $\longrightarrow \$850$
1% $\longrightarrow \$8.50$
60% $\longrightarrow \$510$

Mrs. Smith spent $510 on the gifts.

7. a. $\underline{100\%} - \underline{15\%} = \underline{85\%}$

$\underline{85}\%$ of the meat was kept in the refrigerator.

b. **Method 1:**

$\underline{85}\% \times \underline{240}$ kg

$= \frac{85}{100} \times 240$ kg $= \underline{204}$ kg

$\underline{204}$ kilograms of meat were kept in the refrigerator.

Method 2:

100% $\longrightarrow \underline{240}$
1% $\longrightarrow \underline{2.4}$
85% $\longrightarrow \underline{204}$

$\underline{204}$ kilograms of meat were kept in the refrigerator.

8. a. 100% $-$ (55% + 22%) = 23%

23% of the students were Hispanic.

b. 23% of 800

$= \frac{23}{100} \times 800 = 184$

184 of the students were Hispanic.

9. 100% $-$ (45% + 42%) = 13%

13% of $2,000 $= \frac{13}{100} \times \$2,000 = \$260$

Mr. Anderson saved $260.

Worksheet 4

1. 4% of $1,600 $= \frac{4}{100} \times \$1,600 = \$64$

Mr. Taylor will get $64 after 1 year.

2. 6% of $1,200 $= \frac{6}{100} \times \$1,200 = \$72$

a. Ms. Benjamin will get $72 in interest after 1 year.

b. $1,200 + $72 $-$ $1,272

Ms. Benjamin will have $1,272 in the bank after 1 year.

3. 5% of $800 $= \frac{5}{100} \times \$800 = \$40$

Benny paid $40 in sales tax.

4. a. 5% of $\$1,500 = \dfrac{5}{100} \times \$1,500$

    $= \$75$

    Lisa paid $\$75$ in sales tax.

    b. $\$1,500 + \$75 = \$1,575$

    Lisa paid $\$1,575$ in total.

5. 15% of $\$1,200 = \dfrac{15}{100} \times \$1,200$

    $= \$180$

    The dollar amount of the discount was $\$180$.

6. 20% of $\$4,200 = \dfrac{20}{100} \times \$4,200$

    $= \$840$

    The dollar amount of the discount was $\$840$.

    a. $\$4,200 - \$840 = \$3,360$

    The discounted price for the piano was $\$3,360$.

    b. 5% of $\$3,360 = \dfrac{5}{100} \times \$3,360$

    $= \$168$

    She paid $\$168$ in sales tax.

Chapter 11

Worksheet 1

1. 1
2. $5\dfrac{3}{4}$
3. 9 pounds
4. 6 bags
5.

	Butter X	Butter Y
Weight (lb)	$\dfrac{1}{4}$	$\dfrac{3}{4}$
Number of Sticks	5	3

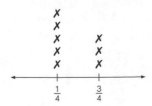

Emma's Butter by Weight

6.

	Juice A	Juice B	Juice C	Juice D
Volume of Bottles (qt)	$\dfrac{1}{4}$	$\dfrac{1}{2}$	$\dfrac{3}{8}$	$\dfrac{3}{4}$
Number of Bottles	3	1	2	4

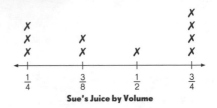

Sue's Juice by Volume

7. 10 bottles
8. $\dfrac{3}{4}$ quart
9. 3 quarts
10. 5 quarts
11. $\dfrac{1}{2}$ quart
12. 14 packages
13. $\dfrac{3}{8}$ lb
14. $1\dfrac{1}{4}$ lb
15. $5\dfrac{1}{8}$ lb
16. 30 lb

Worksheet 2

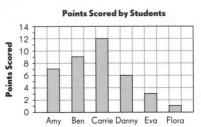

Points Scored by Students

1. Carrie
2. Flora
3. 5
4. Ben
5. 5
6. 5

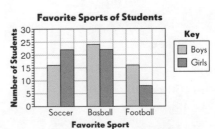

Favorite Sports of Students

7. 22
8. Baseball; 8
9. Baseball
10. Football
11. 52
12. 56

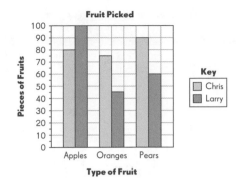

Fruit Picked

13. 245
14. Chris; 40
15. Pears; Apples
16. Oranges
17. 15
18. 60
19. Chris needs 55 pieces of fruit and Larry needs 95 pieces of fruit. Larry needs to pick the greater number of pieces of fruit.
20. Answers vary. Sample: You can find how many pieces of each fruit each boy needs to pick to get to 100 and add those amounts. You can add all the pieces of fruit each boy has picked and subtract that amount from 300.

Worksheet 3

1. $P\,(\underline{4},\,\underline{8})$
2. $Q\,(\underline{8},\,\underline{4})$
3. $R\,(\underline{0},\,\underline{5})$
4. $S\,(\underline{5},\,\underline{0})$

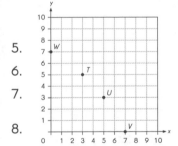

5.
6.
7.
8.

Number of Bottles Needed

9. 3
10. 3.75
11. 20
12. 12
13. 1.875

Worksheet 4

1. $y = 4x$

x	1	2	3	4	5
y	4	8	12	16	20

$y = 7x$

x	1	2	3	4	5
y	7	14	21	28	35

2.

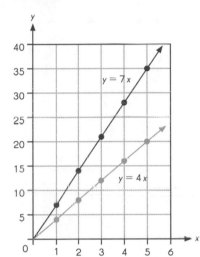

3. 16 and 28
4. 5 and $\dfrac{20}{7}$
5. $49 - 28 = 21$

Jacob's and Sarah's Savings over Five Weeks

6. Week 3
7. 8
8. 70
9. 36; 48
10. Jacob; 10

Worksheet 5

1.

Socks	Ties	Combinations
Red		Red/Blue
Black	Blue	Black/Blue
Green		Green/Blue
Red		Red/Brown
Black	Brown	Black/Brown
Green		Green/Brown

   6

2. 4; 2

3. a.

Drinks	Food	Combinations
Coffee	Cheese	Coffee/Cheese
	Biscuits	Coffee/Biscuits
	Fruit	Coffee/Fruit
Tea	Cheese	Tea/Cheese
	Biscuits	Tea/Biscuits
	Fruit	Tea/Fruit

   b. There are six combinations in all.

4. a. $4 \times 5 = 20$
   b. $5 \times 6 = 30$
   c. $4 \times 6 = 24$

Worksheet 6

1. (H, T), (H, H), (T, H), (T, T); 4

2. $\frac{1}{2}$

3. $\frac{1}{4}$

4. $\frac{1}{4}$

5. (H, 1), (H, 2), (H, 3), (H, 4), (H, 5), (H, 6),
   (T, 1), (T, 2), (T, 3), (T, 4), (T, 5), (T, 6); 12

6. $\frac{1}{4}$

7. $\frac{1}{3}$

8. $\frac{1}{4}$

9. $\frac{9}{20}$

10. $\frac{11}{20}$

11.

Number	Jenny's Outcomes	Experimental Probability	Trish's Outcomes	Experimental Probability
1	8	$\frac{8}{45}$	7	$\frac{7}{45}$
2	9	$\frac{1}{5}$	8	$\frac{8}{45}$
3	8	$\frac{8}{45}$	8	$\frac{8}{45}$
4	6	$\frac{2}{15}$	7	$\frac{7}{45}$
5	5	$\frac{1}{9}$	6	$\frac{2}{15}$
6	9	$\frac{1}{5}$	9	$\frac{1}{5}$

12. Answers vary.

   Sample: Harris spins the spinner 100 times.

   Number of times the spinner lands on:

   Red   52

   Green   25

   Yellow 23

Chapter 12

Worksheet 1

1. m∠EXA = 120°
   m∠AXC = 60°
   $\overleftrightarrow{EC}$ is a line because
   m∠EXA + m∠AXC = 180°.

2. m∠a = 119°
   m∠b = 180° − 119° = 61°

3. m∠a = 124°
   m∠b = 180° − 124° = 56°

4. m∠t = 180° − 66° = 114°

5. m∠AOC = 180° − 134° = 46°

6. m∠x = 40°
   m∠y = 90° − m∠x
       = 90° − 40°
       = 50°

7. m∠x = 28°
   m∠y = 90° − m∠x
       = 90° − 28°
       = 62°

8. m∠DBC = 90° − 58° = 32°

9. m∠CBD = 90° − 27° = 63°

10. $m\angle y + \underline{131°} = 180°$

    $m\angle y = \underline{180°} - 131° = \underline{49°}$

11. $m\angle y + \underline{164°} = 180°$

    $m\angle y = \underline{180°} - 164° = \underline{16°}$

12. $m\angle x = 90° - 25° - 18° = 47°$

13. $m\angle x = 180° - 45° - 34° = 101°$

14.

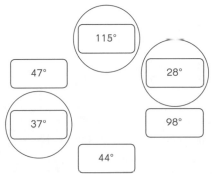

Worksheet 2

1. $m\angle \underline{SOP} + m\angle \underline{POQ} + m\angle \underline{QOR} + m\angle \underline{ROS}$
    $= 360°$

2. $m\angle POQ + m\angle QOR + m\angle ROS + m\angle SOP$
    $= \underline{100°} + \underline{80°} + \underline{100°} + \underline{80°}$
    $= \underline{360°}$

3. $m\angle s = \underline{122°}$
    $m\angle t = 360° - m\angle s$
         $= 360° - \underline{122°}$
         $= \underline{238°}$

4. $m\angle s = \underline{55°}$
    $m\angle t = 360° - m\angle s$
         $= 360° - \underline{55°}$
         $= \underline{305°}$

5. $m\angle x = \underline{360°} - 115° = \underline{245°}$

6. $m\angle PQR = \underline{360°} - \underline{245°} = \underline{115°}$

7. $m\angle x = 180° - 98° = 82°$
    $m\angle y = 180° - 82° = 98°$
    $m\angle z = 180° - 98° = 82°$

8. $m\angle x = 360° - 154° - 42° - 108° = 56°$

9. $m\angle x = 180° - 28° - 115° = 37°$

10.

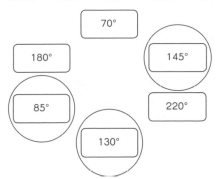

Worksheet 3

1. $m\angle \underline{AXB} = m\angle \underline{DXC}$
    $m\angle \underline{AXD} = m\angle \underline{BXC}$

2.

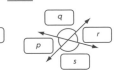

3. $m\angle \underline{w} = m\angle \underline{y}$
    $m\angle \underline{x} = m\angle \underline{z}$

4. $m\angle YOZ = 180° - 32° = \underline{148°}$
    $m\angle WOX = m\angle YOZ = \underline{148°}$

5. $m\angle AOD = 180° - 143° = \underline{37°}$
    $m\angle COD = m\angle AOB = \underline{143°}$
    $m\angle BOC = m\angle AOD = \underline{37°}$

6. $m\angle x = 360° - 136° - 42° - 90° = 92°$

7. $m\angle AOD - 86° - 28° = 58°$
    $m\angle x = m\angle AOD = 58°$

8. $m\angle UOV = 58° - 28° = 30°$
    $m\angle TOU = 100° - 30° = 70°$
    $m\angle SOT = 180° - 58° - 70° = 52°$

Chapter 13

Worksheet 1

1.	True	2.	True
3.	False	4.	True
5.	False	6.	✔
7.	◯	8.	◯
9.	True	10.	False
11.	True	12.	True
13.	✔	14.	✔
15.	◯	16.	True
17.	True	18.	✔
19.	◯	20.	✔
21.	True	22.	False
23.	False	24.	✔
25.	◯	26.	✔
27.	False	28.	True
29.	◯	30.	✔

31. ☐   32. False

33. True   34. ☐

35. ☑   36. ☐

Worksheet 2

1. True   2. True

3. False   4. True

5. 62°   6. 110°

7. 37°   8. 37°

9. 32°

10. a. 45°   b. 45°

11. Answers vary. Sample: *ABD*; *ADB*; *BAD*

12. False   13. True

14. True

15. *PQS*; *QPS*; *QSP*

16. *QRS*; *QSR*; *SQR*

17. *PRS*; *RSP*; *SPR*

18. *SPR*; *PRS*; *QSP*; *QSR*

19. True   20. True

21. Answers vary. Accept any two angle measures with a sum of 100°.

22. Answers vary. Accept any two angle measures with a sum of 100°.

23. Answers vary. Accept any two angle measures with a sum of 100°.

Worksheet 3

1. 22   2. 155

3. 45   4. 50

5. m∠*FEG* = <u>51</u>°, m∠*EFG* = <u>51</u>°

6. 64   7. 77

8. a. m∠*C* = 55°
   b. m∠*DAC* = 35°

9. a. m∠*C* = 37.5°
   b. m∠*ADB* = 62.5°

10. m∠*b* = 60°   11. m∠*c* = 60°

12. m∠*d* = 120°; m∠*e* = 120°; m∠*f* = 120°

13. m∠*g* = 30°   14. m∠*h* = 83°

15. m∠*i* = 308°; m∠*j* = 284°

16. m∠*k* = 222°   17. m∠*l* = 93°

Worksheet 4

1. 5   2. 7

3. 3   4. 12

5. 10   6. 8

7. Yes   8. Yes

9. Yes

10. 2 in. + 3 in. = 5 in.
   5 in. = 5 in.
   3 in. + 5 in. = 8 in.
   8 in. > 2 in.
   2 in. + 5 in. = 7 in.
   7 in. > 3 in.

This triangle cannot be formed. The sum of one pair of the sides is equal to the third side.

11. 4 cm + 5 cm = 9 cm
   9 cm < 10 cm
   5 cm + 10 cm = 15 cm
   15 cm > 4 cm
   4 cm + 10 cm = 14 cm
   14 cm > 5 cm

This triangle cannot be formed. The sum of one pair of the sides is less than the third side.

12. 6 cm + 7 cm = 13 cm
   13 cm > 8 cm
   7 cm + 8 cm = 15 cm
   15 cm > 6 cm
   6 cm + 8 cm = 14 cm
   14 cm > 7 cm

This triangle can be formed.

13. *AB* + *BC* = 5 in. + 6 in.
           = 11 in.
   AB + *BC* > *AC*
   11 in. > *AC*

So, *AC* is greater than 4 inches and less than 11 inches. The possible lengths of *AC* are 5 inches, 6 inches, 7 inches, 8 inches, 9 inches, and 10 inches.

14. *XY* + *YZ* = 11 cm + 15 cm
           = 26 cm
   XY + *YZ* > *XZ*
   26 cm > *XZ*

So, *XZ* is greater than 20 centimeters and less than 26 centimeters. The possible lengths of *XZ* are 21 centimeters, 22 centimeters, 23 centimeters, 24 centimeters, and 25 centimeters.

Worksheet 5

1. False   2. False
3. True   4. True
5. ◯   6. ✔
7. $m\angle b = 42°$; $m\angle c = 138°$
8. $m\angle d = 100°$; $m\angle e = 42°$
9. $m\angle f = 87°$; $m\angle g = 45°$
10. $m\angle h = 62°$; $m\angle i = 42°$
11. True   12. False
13. True   14. True
15. True
16. ✔   17. ◯
18. $m\angle b = 32°$; $m\angle c = 32°$
19. $m\angle d = 28°$; $m\angle e = 124°$
20. $m\angle f = 28°$; $m\angle g = 62°$;
    $m\angle h = 118°$
21. $m\angle i = 36°$; $m\angle j = 54°$
22. False   23. False
24. False   25. False
26. False   27. ◯
28. ✔   29. $m\angle y = 38°$
30. $m\angle p = 96°$; $m\angle q = 33°$;
    $m\angle r = 19°$
31. $m\angle p = 62°$
32. $m\angle q = 59°$
33. $m\angle r = 44°$; $m\angle s = 46°$
34. $m\angle t = 61°$; $m\angle u = 58°$
35. $m\angle v = 142°$; $m\angle w = 52°$

Chapter 14

Worksheet 1

1. 12   2. 11   3. 9   4. 5
5. 8   6. 10   7. 5   8. 10
9. 16   10. 17

Worksheet 2

1.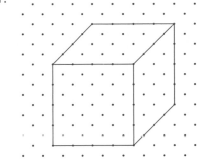

2.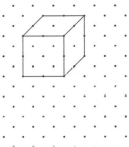

3.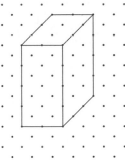

4.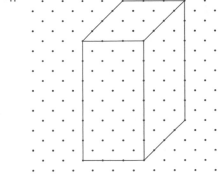

5.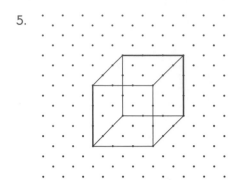

6.

7.

Worksheet 3

1. Answers vary. Sample:

2. (Triangle) (Square) Rectangle
   Parallelogram Pentagon Hexagon

3.

4.

5. Rectangular prism

   Pentagonal prism

   Triangular prism

   Octagonal prism

   Hexagonal prism

	Type of Prism	Number of Faces	Number of Edges	Number of Vertices
6.	Rectangular	6	12	8
7.	Pentagonal	7	15	10
8.	Triangular	5	9	6
9.	Octagonal	10	24	16
10.	Hexagonal	8	18	12

11.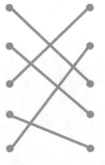

12. Triangular pyramid

    Rectangular pyramid

    Pentagonal pyramid

    Hexagonal pyramid

    Octagonal pyramid

	Type of Pyramid	Number of Faces	Number of Edges	Number of Vertices
13.	Triangular	4	6	4
14.	Rectangular	5	8	5
15.	Pentagonal	6	10	6
16.	Hexagonal	7	12	7
17.	Octagonal	9	16	9

18.

19. Answers vary.
Sample:

20.
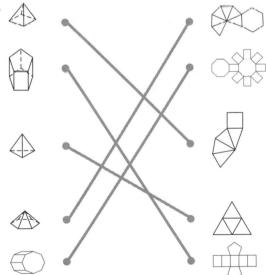

21. a. The base of a rectangular prism is a rectangle. The base of a cube is a square. A square is also a rectangle. Thus, a cube is also considered a rectangular prism.
b. A cone does not have two parallel bases, thus is not a prism.

22. The pyramid and cylinder are not prisms. They do not have parallel bases that are polygons. The last two figures are prisms because each has two parallel bases that are congruent polygons.

Worksheet 4

1. 294 cm²
2. 1,176 in.²
3. 460 in.²
4. 1,122 in.²
5. 278 m²
6. 576 cm²
7. 546 in.²
8. (110 cm × 85 cm + 85 cm × 40 cm + 110 cm × 40 cm) × 2 = 34,300 cm²
The surface area of the cupboard is 34,300 square centimeters.
9. 96 cm × 78 cm + (78 cm × 34 cm + 96 cm × 34 cm) × 2 = 19,320 cm²
The surface area of the outside of the cabinet without the cover is 19,320 square centimeters.
10. (12 ft × 7 ft + 8.5 ft × 7 ft) × 2 − 2 × 6.5 ft = 274 ft²
The surface area of the walls in the room is 274 square feet.

Worksheet 5

1. 7
2. 8
3. 9
4. 9
5. 10
6. 11
7. 13
8. 16
9. 7; 13; C; D
10. 12; 19; F; E
11. 5; 3; 4; 60; 4; 2; 3; 24; G; H
12. 3; 3; 3; 27; 5; 5; 4; 100; K; M

Worksheet 6

1. 17,010 cm³
2. 2,197 m³
3. 11,400 m³
4. 23,712 in.³
5. 729 in.³
6. 12,852 ft³
7. 3,375 ft³
8. 8 cm × 4.5 cm × 6 cm
= 216 cm³
= 216 mL
= 0 L 216 mL
The capacity of the fish tank is 0 liters 216 milliliters.
9. 6 cm × 3.5 cm × 12 cm
= 252 cm³
= 252 mL
= 0 L 252 mL
There are 0 liters 252 milliliters of water in the container.

10. 15 cm × 9 cm × 13 cm
    = 1,755 cm^3
    = 1,755 mL
    = 1 L 755 mL

    There are 1 liter 755 milliliters of glue in the box.

11. $\frac{1}{2}$ × 12 cm × 15 cm × 8 cm
    = 720 cm^3 = 720 mL

    720 milliliters of water are needed to fill up the container.
    $\frac{1}{3}$ × 12 cm × 15 cm × 8 cm
    = 480 cm^3 = 480 mL
    720 mL × 2 − 480 mL = 960 mL

    960 milliliters of water must be poured out so that the container is $\frac{1}{3}$ full.

12. $\frac{1}{2} - \frac{1}{4} = \frac{1}{4}$

    8 × 27 cm^3 = 216 cm^3

    $\frac{1}{4}$ ➝ 216 cm^3

    $\frac{4}{4}$ ➝ 216 cm^3 × 4 = 864 cm^3

    The capacity of the tank is 864 cubic centimeters.

13. Current volume of water

    = $\frac{2}{3}$ × 50 m × 25 m × 12 m

    − 5 m × 3 m × 25 m

    = 9,625 m^3
    Final volume of water
    = 50 m × 25 m × 5 m − 5 m × 3 m × 25 m
    = 5,875 m^3
    9,625 m^3 − 5,875 m^3
    = 3,750 m^3
    3,750 cubic meters of water must be drained off.

14. a. length × <u>width</u> × <u>height</u>
    b. <u>length</u> × width × <u>height</u>

15. Answers vary. Sample: height, length; height, length, width

16. 504

17. 324 yd^3

Worksheet 7

1. a. <u>8</u> × <u>16</u> × <u>12</u> = <u>1,536</u> cm^3
   b. <u>5</u> × <u>8</u> × <u>6</u> = <u>240</u> cm^3
   c. <u>1,536</u> + <u>240</u> = <u>1,776</u> cm^3

2. 540 cm^3 − 64 cm^3 = 476 cm^3

3. 540 in.^{3} + 810 in.^{3} = 1,350 in.^{3}